21572

5, 20, 15

£5.85.

DATE DUE FOR RETURN

THERMAL EXPANSION

Monographs in Low-Temperature Physics

Edited by John G. Daunt
Stevens Institute of Technology
Hoboken, New Jersey
and
K. Mendelssohn
The University of Oxford
Oxford, England

Bernard Yates — Thermal Expansion — 1972

THERMAL EXPANSION

Bernard Yates

Department of Pure and Applied Physics
University of Salford
Lancashire, England

ℚ PLENUM PRESS • NEW YORK-LONDON • 1972

Library of Congress Catalog Card Number 70-179759

ISBN 0-306-30550-X

© 1972 Plenum Press, New York
A Division of Plenum Publishing Corporation
227 West 17th Street, New York, N.Y. 10011

United Kingdom edition published by Plenum Press, London
A Division of Plenum Publishing Company, Ltd.
Davis House (4th Floor), 8 Scrubs Lane, NW10 6SE, London, England

Printed in the United States of America

Preface

The subject of thermal expansion is one about which relatively little has been written, for although quite precise measurements have been made over the last hundred years or so, it is only in comparatively recent times that a deep appreciation of such work has developed. The temperature range of the investigations has been extended from the vicinity of room temperature down to very low temperatures and up to very high temperatures, and the last few years in particular have seen a marked increase in the applications of means of measuring small dimensional changes.

One of the prime objectives of this book is to summarize some of the advances which have been made in the subject; however, the fundamental information conveyed about the vibrations of atoms and molecules in solids by the study of thermal expansion taken in isolation is much less than is possible by considering the phenomenon in association with the study of specific heat and elastic constants. For this reason the treatment of thermal expansion is approached via the more familiar subject of specific heat, and this is followed by a consideration of elastic constants. Our consideration of thermal expansion there completes a summary of the physical properties required to define the Grüneisen parameter. The account proceeds by examining the information which may be derived about the moments of the vibrational frequency spectra of simple solids and their volume dependence by applying the data within the quasiharmonic approximation, which takes into account the volume dependence of the frequencies.

Finally, the successful extension of this approach to yield information on the explicit temperature dependence of the vibrations is summarized, in association with recent experimental evidence. Although no claim to completeness is made, it is hoped that the treatment will prove to be useful both to undergraduates and to postgraduate workers who wish to gain an introduction to the vibrational properties of solids, access to which is afforded by a study of specific heat, thermal expansion, and elastic constants.

I wish to record my gratitude to the authors who kindly granted me permission to use figures from their publication, to Mr. B. W. James for reading the manuscript and making a number of useful suggestions, and to my wife for checking the manuscript.

B. Y.

Contents

Chapter 4

The Thermal Expansion of Solids 51

Chapter 5

The Analysis of Thermodynamic Data 73

Chapter 6

The Quantitative Study of Anharmonic Effects 91

Chapter 1

Introduction

1.1. GENERAL REMARKS

The subject of thermal expansion is one which is difficult to discuss in complete isolation, since an appreciation of the phenomenon, its origins, and its conscquences is closely related to other thermodynamic properties of matter. Of these other properties, the phenomenon of specific heat has probably received the greatest deal of attention, and the reasons for this are not difficult to understand. The need for a knowledge of the specific heat of a solid occurs repeatedly in thermodynamic arguments, in solid-state theory, and in a variety of practical scientific and engineering applications. In this sense the thermal expansion of solids has occupied a position of secondary importance in comparison. However, both for fundamental and pragmatic reasons, interest in the subject has grown steadily in recent years and the challenges presented to theoreticians and experimentalists alike have stimulated exciting developments which have extended beyond the bounds of their own immediate fields. It will be convenient to approach the subject by considering first the vibrations of atoms in solids in general terms.

1.2. BASIC IDEAS CONCERNING THE VIBRATIONS OF ATOMS IN SOLIDS

If we begin by concentrating attention on a single crystal of a reasonably simple solid, we find that the atoms or ions are arranged in a regular three-dimensional array. Consider, for example, a crystal of sodium chloride.

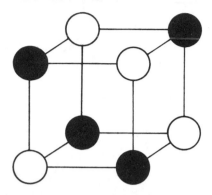

Fig. 1. Arrangement of the ions in the sodium chloride lattice: ●, Na⁺ ions; ○, Cl⁻ ions.

Figure 1 depicts the ions at their equilibrium positions, but in fact they are vibrating about these mean positions. As the temperature of the crystal is raised more thermal energy is injected into the crystal, the ions vibrate with greater and greater amplitude, and the mean distance of separation of the ions increases. Eventually the amplitudes become sufficiently large to overcome the restraining forces which hold the solid together, and the solid melts. A simple mechanism of thermal expansion in a linear chain is illustrated in Fig. 2, in which a_1 and a_2 may be taken to represent the amplitudes of oscillation at corresponding temperatures T_1 and T_2, where $a_2 > a_1$. The potential energy ϕ of the assembly may be written as a function of the displacement of a typical particle from its equilibrium position, which in turn may be expressed as a series expansion, i.e.,

$$\phi = f(a)$$
$$= pa + qa^2 + ra^3 + \cdots \tag{1.1}$$

in which p, q, r, etc. are constants. If the restoring force at zero displacement is to be zero, the coefficient p must be zero, and Eq. (1.1) reduces to

$$\phi = qa^2 + ra^3 + \cdots$$

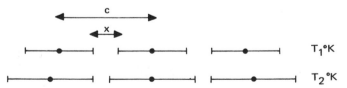

Fig. 2. Schematic linear representation of atoms, in which displacements $a = (c - x)/2$ from their equilibrium positions at temperatures $T_1(°K)$ and $T_2(°K)$, illustrating the increase in mean separation of the atoms and the increase of amplitudes of vibration accompanying a rise of temperature from T_1 to T_2.

If all coefficients of a beyond q were zero, the equation would reduce to $\phi = qa^2$, which would correspond to the simple harmonic oscillation of the atoms in which the potential energy of a displaced atom was proportional to the second power only of its displacement from the equilibrium position. This is commonly called the *harmonic approximation*. Such a crystal would display no thermal expansion, and in order to make our system bear some relationship to the real physical world we must include the term in r and subsequent terms, known as the *anharmonic terms*. As the temperature rises, the amplitudes of oscillation will increase, and the anharmonic effects will become more important.

In the analysis of thermodynamic data it is frequently convenient to define a harmonic heat capacity, which is based upon experimentally observed specific heats in the approximate temperature region $\theta^C/6$ to $\theta^C/3$, where θ^C is the approximate Debye characteristic temperature of the solid, determined from its specific heat. Such data may be fitted to the high-temperature quasiharmonic expansion

$$(\theta^C)^2 = (\theta^C_\infty)^2[1 + (A/T^2) + (B/T^4) + \cdots] \tag{1.2}$$

in which θ^C_∞ is the high-temperature limiting value of θ^C, T is the absolute temperature, and A, B, etc. are constants. Data corresponding to much lower temperatures would not allow Eq. (1.2) to converge sufficiently rapidly for most practical purposes; however, experience has shown that at much higher temperatures the anharmonic contribution to the heat capacity becomes significant in comparison with the harmonic contribution. It is important to realize, however, as Barron (1964) has pointed out, that at temperatures of the order of $\theta^C/3$ the thermal energy of a solid, E_T is only about one-third of the zero-point energy E_Z, and the mean amplitude of vibration of the atoms is not much different from the value at $T = 0$.

Since the idea of a sudden onset of anharmonicity is physically unacceptable, one must therefore conclude that an anharmonic contribution to the heat capacity must be present down to $T = 0$. For this reason harmonic specific heats deriving their origin from an analysis of experimental data in the approximate temperature range $\theta^C/6$ to $\theta^C/3$ are not harmonic in any absolute sense. They correspond to an effective frequency distribution which is consistent with the assumptions implicit in the quasiharmonic approximation, into which results may be fed from the real physical world and from which results emerge which accord closely with experimental findings. This self-consistency leads to the conclusion that this effective distribution must bear a close resemblance to physical reality, and that anharmonic effects do not in general appear to have reached serious proportions at $T \approx \theta^C/3$. We shall return to a more detailed consideration of anharmonic effects in solids later. Meanwhile, following the point made in the opening remarks, a discussion of effects such as consequences of anharmonic effects will be greatly facilitated by summarizing some of the more important basic ideas concerning two closely related phenomena, specific heat and elastic constants. Together with a knowledge of the thermal expansion of a solid, these will yield valuable information concerning the volume variation of the frequencies of lattice vibrations and other properties of vibrational frequency spectra. Specific heat will be considered first.

Incidentally, we may note in passing that if we assume that the Nernst heat theorem applies to the solids in which we are primarily interested, it follows that the volume coefficient thermal expansion of these solids must approach zero as the absolute zero of temperature is approached. For if ΔS represents the increase in entropy which accompanies an isothermal change in the physical state of a solid, then, provided that the internal stability has not been influenced by the change, we may write

$$\lim_{T \to 0} \Delta S = 0$$

On this basis we should expect that

$$\lim_{T \to 0} \left(\frac{\partial S}{\partial P} \right)_T = 0$$

and since

$$\beta = \frac{1}{V} \left(\frac{\partial V}{\partial T} \right)_P = - \frac{1}{V} \left(\frac{\partial S}{\partial P} \right)_T$$

where β is the volume coefficient of thermal expansion and the other terms have their usual meanings, it follows that $\beta \to 0$ as $T \to 0$.

The Representation of Specific Heat

2.1. THE BEHAVIOR OF THE LATTICE

In order to understand current representations of specific heat phenomena it will be useful to consider briefly the background against which these arose. The empirical rule of Dulong and Petit, formulated in 1819, stated that the atomic heats of a large number of elements were equal to approximately 6 cal (g-atom)$^{-1}$ °C^{-1}. A theoretical explanation was provided later by the theorem of the equipartition of energy, which predicted that $C_V = 3R$, R being the gas constant. However, when specific heat measurements were extended to below room temperature it became clear that the rule of Dulong and Petit did not hold at low temperatures. It was observed, however, that a good approximation for a large number of substances is

$$C_V \approx f(T/\theta) \tag{2.1}$$

where f was the same function for a wide range of substances, but each substance had its own characteristic value of θ. Typical values of θ for a number of solids are shown in Table 1.

Replacing each atom in the solid by three "oscillators," Einstein applied quantum theory to the problem in 1907. He took the mean energy of the $3N$ oscillations of a gram atom to be

$$\bar{U} = h\nu/(e^{h\nu/kT} - 1) \tag{2.2}$$

where N is Avogadro's number, h is Planck's constant, k is Boltzmann's constant, and ν is the frequency of vibration of a typical oscillator. The

Table 1. Approximate Values of the High-Temperature Limiting Values of the Debye Characteristic Temperatures θ_∞^C for a Number of Common Substances

Substance	θ_∞^C, °K	Substance	θ_∞^C, °K
Pyrolytic graphite	1975	KI	163
Al	418	CaWO$_4$	235
Fe	467	ZnO	706
Cu	339	RbBr	140
Cd	300	CdS	365
Pb	94	CsCl	180
NaF	438	CsBr	144
NaCl	290	CsI	101
NaI	195	CaF$_2$	490
KCl	236	SrF$_2$	418
KBr	188	BaF$_2$	360

expression for the gram-atomic heat thus became

$$C_V = \left(\frac{d\bar{U}}{dT}\right)_V = 3R\left(\frac{h\nu}{kT}\right)^2 \frac{e^{h\nu/kT}}{(e^{h\nu/kT} - 1)^2} \tag{2.3}$$

i.e., $C_V = 3Rf(T/\theta_E)$, where the "Einstein temperature" $\theta_E = h\nu_E/k$. When $T \gg \theta_E$, $C_V \to 3R$, in agreement with the classical result at high temperatures. When $T \ll \theta_E$, $C_V \to 3R(\theta_E/T)^2 e^{-\theta_E/T}$, which does not fit the experimental results well because the assumption of a single vibrational frequency for all of the atoms is too drastic. In fact there must be strong forces between the atoms of a solid and the motion of any one of them will influence the motion of its neighbors. Born and von Kármán (1912, 1913) took account of these forces as well as of the discrete nature of the lattice in deriving an expression for the specific heat of a solid. Because of its greater simplicity, the theory of Debye (1912) has received wider publicity than that of Born and von Kármán, although the approach of the latter is much more rigorous.

Debye began by regarding the solid as being continuous, isotropic, and elastic. Multiplying the number of normal modes of vibration per unit volume having frequencies between ν and $\nu + d\nu$ by the average energy per oscillator yielded by quantum theory [given in Eq. (2.2)] gives the energy of vibrations in the frequency range ν to $\nu + d\nu$ as

$$4\pi\left(\frac{1}{c_l^3} + \frac{2}{c_t^3}\right)\left(\frac{h\nu^3}{e^{h\nu/kT} - 1}\right) d\nu \tag{2.4}$$

per unit volume, where c_l and c_t are the velocities of longitudinal and transverse vibrations, respectively. He then assumed that all vibrational frequencies between zero and a maximum value ν_D were possible, following which he proceeded to take account of the discontinuous structure of matter by relating this number to the number of individual atoms, assuming that each of these had three degrees of freedom. Combining the consequences of these assumptions led to the expression

$$U = \frac{9N}{\nu_D{}^3} \int_0^{\nu_D} \frac{h\nu^3}{e^{h\nu/kT} - 1}\, d\nu \tag{2.5}$$

for the total energy U of a gram atom. Differentiating with respect to T gives

$$C_V = \frac{9N}{\nu_D{}^3} \int_0^{\nu_D} \frac{(h^2\nu^4/kT^2)e^{h\nu/kT}}{(e^{h\nu/kT} - 1)^2}\, d\nu \tag{2.6}$$

Putting $x = h\nu/kT$, $\theta = h\nu_D/k$, and integrating Eq. (2.6) by parts gives

$$C_V = 9Nk\left[4\left(\frac{T}{\theta}\right)^3 \int_0^{\theta/T} \frac{x^3\, dx}{e^x - 1} - \frac{\theta}{T}\frac{1}{e^{\theta/T} - 1}\right] \tag{2.7}$$

It will be seen that Eq. (2.7) is of the form observed experimentally and summarized in Eq. (2.1), which we may write in the form $C_V = 3Rf(T/\theta)$, where some physical significance has now been given to the parameter associated with the temperature through

$$\theta = h\nu_D/k \tag{2.8}$$

It is worth noting that when $T < \theta/12$, $C_V \approx (12\pi^4Nk/5)(T/\theta)^3$ to an accuracy of approximately 1%, and when $T \gg \theta_D$, $C_V \rightarrow 3Nk = 3R$, which agrees with the rule of Dulong and Petit. In spite of the simplifications made, the remarkable success of the theory has earned it a central position in the theory of specific heats, and the behavior of real solids is frequently described in terms of deviations from Debye behavior, rather than in entirely different terms. Major differences between the Debye theory and the other theories mentioned are illustrated in Fig. 3 and 4. Figure 3 compares the Debye and Einstein functions, the former providing the best fit with experiment. Figure 4 shows how different cutoff frequencies are associated with transverse and longitudinal vibrations in the Born–von Kármán theory. This discrimination is not made in the Debye theory. When attempts were made to fit Eq. (2.7) to experimental specific heat data two shortcomings of the theory became evident: (a) results for metals at low temperatures did not fit the theory at all well, and (b) in the case of results for dielectric

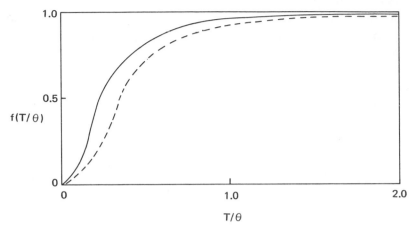

Fig. 3. Figurative representation of the variation of the Debye and Einstein functions with reduced temperature T/θ, in which $C_V = f(T/\theta)$: (——) Debye function; (— —) Einstein function.

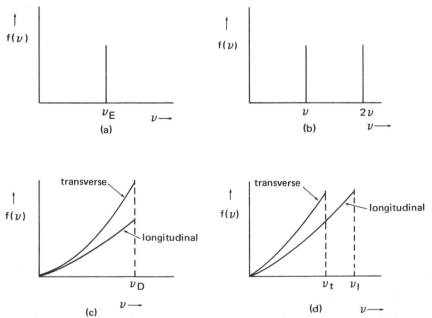

Fig. 4. The frequency distribution functions $f(\nu)$ corresponding to the theories of (a) Einstein, (b) Nernst and Lindemann, (c) Debye and (d) Born and von Kármán. The difference between the high-frequency cutoff in the Debye theory and in the Born—von Kármán theory is illustrated in (c) and (d).

solids, which fit the theory best, it was usually necessary to assume a temperature variation of θ in order to improve the fit of Eq. (2.7) to the observations.

Maintaining some semblance of chronological order, mention may be made of the work of Blackman (1935a, b; 1937a, b) at this stage. Blackman directed his attention to the derivation of the frequency spectrum of a one-dimensional, discontinuous structure, followed by a two-dimensional structure, as a guide to what one might expect to find in the more complicated three-dimensional case, which he then considered in the form of a simple cubic lattice. A spectrum which he deduced is shown diagrammatically in Fig. 5a, and is to be compared with the simple picture given by the Debye assumption in Fig. 4c, in which $f(v)$ is the number of normal modes of vibration per unit range of frequency v. One of the important differences between the two pictures is the piling up of frequencies near the cutoff frequency in Blackman's theory. This piling up would be shown by any consideration in which the solid was supposed to be composed of a series of discrete masses. Blackman indicated that a temperature variation of θ of the type shown in Fig. 5(b) would result from this type of frequency spectrum, which may be compared with the Debye picture of a characteristic temperature which does not vary with temperature. It will be seen later that the detailed shape of the curve of θ versus temperature is not always easy to interpret unambiguously. Part of the value of Blackman's findings lay in their generality. Assuming central forces obeying Hooke's law, he showed how the detailed variation of θ with temperature was governed by the ratio of force

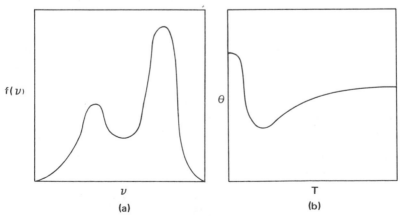

Fig. 5. Representation of Blackman's theory of specific heats: (a) the frequency distribution function $f(v)$ as a function of frequency v and (b) the Debye characteristic temperature θ as a function of temperature T.

constants for nearest and next-nearest neighbors, without considering any particular physical crystal in detail. Later calculations for particular crystal structures agree on this general point of a split of the frequency spectrum into two parts, e.g., Fine (1939) for body-centered cubic tungsten, Kellermann (1941) for the rocksalt structure, Smith (1947) for the diamond structure, and Leighton (1948) for the face-centered cubic structure.

In addition to the reason for the minimum given above, a rising or falling curve of θ^C with temperature at higher temperatures provides a key to a measure of the anharmonic contribution to the heat capacity of a solid consisting of components of comparable mass. On the other hand, in molecular solids similar qualitative evidence may point to the existence of rotational vibration and intramolecular vibrations. In spite of these difficulties of interpretation, one may make some general observations. The theories of Debye and of Blackman are in good agreement for $T < \sim\theta^C_\infty/50$, in which the true, discontinuous structure of matter becomes relatively unimportant to the low-frequency vibrations excited at such temperatures. The fall in θ^C which generally accompanies the rise of T above 0°K indicates that $f(v) \propto v^n$ where $n > 2$, indicating a higher order dependence of the frequency distribution function upon frequency than would be expected on the basis of the Debye theory. This corresponds to the first peak in the spectrum shown in Fig. 5(a). At very high temperatures, on the other hand, at which all the equivalent oscillators in the solid have been excited, one can expect no further increase of C_V to accompany a further rise of temperature. In this case the percentage changes in θ^C corresponding to a given rise of temperature would be expected to diminish in the absence of complications such as those mentioned above.

Attempts to produce improved representations of specific heat phenomena have been made alternatively in terms of Einstein and Debye theories. For purposes of general explanation it might well be though that the association of groups of atoms with different frequencies would give a better representation than the single frequency assumed by Einstein. Following such an approach, Nernst and Lindemann (1911) obtained improved agreement with observation by assuming that half of the resonating atoms had a frequency v and the other half had a frequency $v/2$. In this way they arrived at an expression of the form

$$C_V = \frac{3R}{2}\,\frac{(\theta_N/T)^2 e^{\theta/T}}{(e^{\theta_N/T} - 1)^2} + \frac{\frac{1}{4}(\theta_N/T)^2 e^{\theta_N/2T}}{(e^{\theta_N/2T} - 1)^2}$$

in which θ_N is a different characteristic temperature from those of the Debye

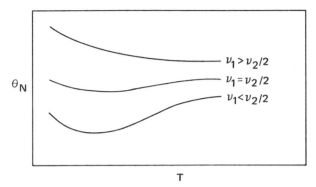

Fig. 6. Representation of the influence of the ratio of the two frequencies assumed in the theory of Nernst and Lindemann upon the temperature variation of the characteristic temperature.

and Einstein theories. Corresponding to this equation, a dip was produced in the graph of characteristic temperature against temperature as shown in Fig. 6.

It has also been found that in the case of a solid consisting of molecules which contained atoms having widely differing masses, such as AgCl, a combination of both an Einstein term and a Debye term produced a better representation of observations than either taken separately. In cases in which the vibrations within a solid arise from different sources it has sometimes been possible to effect a separation by assuming that, to a good approximation, one set of vibrations is approximately monochromatic, capable of representation by an Einstein frequency. Flubacher *et al.* (1960a) effected such a separation for the librational modes of ice molecules. Katz (1951) attempted to improve agreement with observation by modifying the Debye representation to include a series of superimposed Einstein frequencies. At high temperatures the weighted "effective" Einstein frequencies provided parameters which could be used for the comparison of data, although they possessed no direct physical meaning. At low temperatures, however, approximately monochromatic peaks of this type may be associated with physically real structure-sensitive causes, and use has been made of them in interpreting experimental data.

In rigorously applying a reiterative analysis to experimental results for ice, which contains well-defined molecular units, Leadbetter (1965) assumed that the vibrations in the solid arose from three sources: translational vibrations of the molecules, librations of the molecules, and intramolecular vibrations of the atoms. This more comprehensive work than the earlier work of Flubacher *et al.* confirmed the approximately monochromatic nature of the librations. Other results emerging from this work produced agreement between properties of the effective harmonic spectrum and its average total temperature dependence with the results of spectroscopic experiments, and the calculated root mean square amplitudes of vibration of the atoms were in good agreement with the results of X-ray and neutron scattering experiments. This added further support of a general nature for the validity of the association of the effective "harmonic" frequency spectrum, based upon observations of experimental data in the approximate temperature range $\theta^C/6 \leq T \leq \theta^C/3$, with the true spectrum in the solid, as well as providing added proof of the existence of approximately Einsteinian frequencies in real physical situations. An attempt to separate component contributions to the gross vibrational spectrum in a molecular solid has also been made by Lyon and Westrum (1968). They subtracted appropriate Einstein contributions from each of the 18 modes assigned by Scott (1968) from their experimental specific heat curve for calcium tungstate to give the approximate heat capacity due to lattice vibrations only.

Extensive reviews of the theory of the lattice contribution to the specific heats of solids have been given by Blackman (1955) and de Launay (1956b). For the present purpose of recapitulating those aspects of the subject that impinge on an understanding of thermal expansion, it will suffice to summarize the following points. At temperatures below approximately $\theta^C_\infty/50$, at which the discontinuous structure of matter is relatively unimportant to the low-frequency vibrations excited at these temperatures, the Debye assumption of $f(\nu) \propto \nu^2$ is valid, corresponding to a T^3 region in the specific heat curve. This is reflected in a temperature-independent value of θ^C. As the temperature rises, $f(\nu)$ rises more rapidly than ν^2, resulting in θ^C falling with further rise of temperature. θ^C generally reaches a minimum, corresponding to the first of at least two peaks in the graph of $f(\nu)$ against ν, following which it may become independent of temperature, suggesting as one possible explanation the excitation of all the oscillating units of atoms or groups of atoms.

The alkali halides, possessing simple ionic bonding, display the three possible types of temperature variation of θ^C at high temperatures. Among those possessing the face-centered cubic structure, the sodium salts display insensitivity of θ^C to temperature change at these temperatures, (see, e.g., Kirkham and Yates, 1968, for NaF; Morrison and Patterson, 1956, for NaCl; and Berg and Morrison, 1957, for NaI). This may be contrasted with the rapid fall observed by Berg and Morrison (1957) in the potassium salts, and the rises observed in the body-centered cubic alkali halides, CsCl, CsBr, CsI (Taylor et $al.$, 1963; Kirkham and Yates, 1968; Sorai, 1968).

Both the rises and the falls may be ascribed to anharmonic effects, the different temperature dependences presumably arising from the different crystal structures. It has also been mentioned that a falling θ^C could result from librations and intramolecular vibrations in a well-defined molecular solid such as ice, as shown by Leadbetter (1965). The general existence of the two major peaks in the frequency spectrum demonstrated by Blackman and later workers has explained the success of the earlier approach of Nernst and Lindemann, and attention has been drawn to the value of the careful application of approximately monochromatic Einstein-type frequencies in current interpretations of certain heat capacity data. In conclusion, it has been shown by, e.g., Barron and Morrison (1960) and Chambers (1961) that in spite of the great value of specific heat data, their usefulness in permitting a calculation of the vibrational frequency spectrum of a solid is severely limited because of the insensitivity of the temperature variation of the specific heat to fine detail in the spectrum.

2.2. THE BEHAVIOR OF ELECTRONS IN METALS

The discussion has so far been restricted to the energy associated with the vibrations of the constituent units of the lattice, i.e., the atoms or groups of atoms. In the case of a metal a considerable fraction of the total energy of the assembly is contributed by the electrons, particularly at low temperatures, since these are to some extent "free." An appreciation of the origin of this contribution is important in the present context, because of its influence upon the thermal expansion of metals.

Attempts to explain the temperature variation of the magnitude of electronic heats broke down when classical theory was applied to the problem. This assumed that each electron was free and had three degrees of freedom, giving rise to a contribution to the specific heat of $3nkT/2$, where n is the number of electrons concerned. The experimental results could be reconciled more easily with the classical value for the lattice contribution to the specific heat alone at normal temperatures. It was therefore desired to show that any electronic contribution to the specific heat, which might be important at low temperatures, became an almost negligible fraction of the total specific heat at normal temperatures. A great advance was made in 1927 when Sommerfeld applied Fermi–Dirac statistics to the problem.

On the basis of the free-electron approximation, electrons are regarded as existing in states which may be represented by points in six-dimensional phase space. In accordance with Pauli's exclusion principle each electron state can contain two electrons, with two different directions of spin. If each state is to be pictured in three-dimensional momentum space, the state which can accommodate two electrons is represented by an elementary volume h^3/L^3, where L^3 is the uncertainty in the position of an electron. This comes directly from Heisenberg's principle of uncertainty. The classical picture predicts that as the temperature of an assembly of electrons is lowered, the energies and momenta of all the electrons should be reduced to zero, but one is now to imagine the elementary volumes described above receding toward the origin of the momentum diagram as the absolute zero is approached, until, when this temperature is reached, they form a sphere about the origin. Equating the volume of this sphere to the sum of the elementary volumes for a system consisting of n electrons, differentiating the result, introducing a weight factor g to take account of spin direction, and expressing momentum in terms of energy finally gives the standard distribution of states

$$\nu(\varepsilon)\,d\varepsilon = (2\pi g V/h^3)(2m)^{3/2}\varepsilon^{1/2}\,d\varepsilon \qquad (2.9)$$

in which $\nu(\varepsilon)\,d\varepsilon$ is the number of energy states in the energy range $d\varepsilon$ and m is the mass of an electron. This distribution of energy states, in which $\nu(\varepsilon)$ varies as $\varepsilon^{1/2}$, is shown in Fig. 7. In spite of the simplifications made in this deduction, the agreement with the electron distribution curves for the alkali metals, deduced from soft X-ray spectroscopic measurements, is quite reasonable.

The influence of the electrons on the thermal properties of a metal is governed by their distribution among the possible states. We have seen that at the absolute zero of temperature the occupied electron states correspond to a sphere about the origin of momentum space. When the temperature of the system is raised by an amount sufficient to excite electrons from states near the boundary of the sphere to states just outside this boundary the

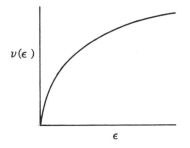

$\nu(\epsilon)$

ϵ

Fig. 7.   Variation of the density of electron energy states $\nu(\varepsilon)$ with energy ε in the standard distribution of states.

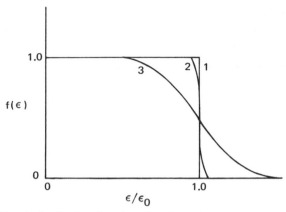

Fig. 8. The Fermi distribution function $f(\varepsilon)$, in which temperatures $T = 0$, $\theta_F/100$, and $\theta_F/10$ are denoted by 1, 2, and 3, respectively.

surface of the sphere will become less clearly defined. With further heat input the energy of the electrons will progressively become sufficient to enable them to travel between states of increasingly greater energy difference. The Fermi distribution function $f(\varepsilon)$ expresses the probability that an electron state is occupied. This is shown diagrammatically in Fig. 8, in which the increasing diffuseness of the bounding surface of the sphere in momentum space is shown by curves 1, 2, and 3 corresponding to increasing the temperature from the absolute zero to several thousand degrees Centigrade. When the temperature is sufficiently high to remove the degeneracy altogether the electrons behave more like a classical gas and may be treated by Maxwell–Boltzmann statistics. The criterion which determines the temperature at which the correct statistics to be applied changes over from Maxwell–Boltzmann to Fermi–Dirac is given by the equation

$$\theta_F = \varepsilon_0/k \qquad (2.10)$$

in which ε_0 is the maximum electron energy in the completely degenerate state. The values in Table 2 have been calculated assuming one electron

Table 2.   Typical Fermi Temperatures θ_F

Metal	θ_F, °K
Sodium	36,600
Silver	63,800
Copper	81,500

per atom and give an idea of the magnitude of θ_F. Applying Fermi–Dirac statistics to an assembly of supposedly free electrons, Stoner (1936a) obtained expressions for the total energy and hence the specific heat of free electrons from the absolute zero up to high temperatures. His high-temperature result may be expressed as the series expansion,

$$C_e = \tfrac{3}{2}Nk\,[1 - 6.65 \times 10^{-2}(\varepsilon_0/kT)^{3/2} + 3.72 \times 10^{-3}(\varepsilon_0/kT)^3 \cdots]$$
$$kT/\varepsilon_0 > 1 \qquad (2.11)$$

which tends toward the classical value of $3Nk/2$ at high temperatures. His low-temperature approximation for the electronic heat capacity takes the form

$$C_e = Nk\,[4.93(kT/\varepsilon_0) - 14.6(kT/\varepsilon_0)^3 - 110(kT/\varepsilon_0)^5], \qquad kT/\varepsilon_0 < 0.38$$
$$(2.12)$$

In a further paper Stoner (1936b) adopted the collective electron approach to specific heat and spin paramagnetism in metals and obtained a low-temperature expression which agreed with the earlier result when the free-electron standard distribution of states was substituted.

The foregoing remarks have been restricted to electrons which move in a field-free region. Useful approximations to the results obtained from experimental measurements of specific heats of metals at low temperatures have been made using equations derived on the free-electron basis. However, more useful information of wider interest may be obtained if account is taken of the fact that the electrons move in a periodic field. Adopting the collective electron approach, the wave equation referred to one electron may be written in the form

$$-(\hbar^2/2m)\,\nabla^2\psi + V(\mathbf{r})\psi = E\psi \qquad (2.13)$$

in which $\hbar = h/2\pi$, $V(\mathbf{r})$ is the potential due to the ions and the average field of the other electrons, and $E\psi$ is the total energy of the assembly. This must obviously have the periodicity of the lattice and we may write

$$V(\mathbf{r}) = V(\mathbf{r} + \mathbf{a})$$

where $\mathbf{a}$ is the length of the vector joining two points of the lattice. The argument may be developed to produce the Sommerfeld approximation for free electrons, into which periodic boundary conditions may then be introduced, producing the results

$$\varepsilon = (h^2/8\pi^2 m)(\mathbf{k}_x^2 + \mathbf{k}_y^2 + \mathbf{k}_z^2) \qquad (2.14)$$

in which k_x, k_y, and k_z are components of $\mathbf{k} = \mathbf{k}_x + \mathbf{k}_y + \mathbf{k}_z$, which is related to momentum $\mathbf{p}$ through

$$|\mathbf{k}| = 2\pi\mathbf{p}/h$$

Equation (2.14) indicates the existence of discrete energy levels for the electron within the atom, but these are so close together that, to a first approximation, ε may be considered to vary continuously with k_x, k_y, and k_z. The idea of a periodic field of the lattice may be introduced as a convenient modification to the foregoing scheme by multiplying the solution to the wave equation, obtained previously, by a periodic function $u_k(\mathbf{r})$, where

$$u_k(\mathbf{r}) = u_k(\mathbf{r} + \mathbf{a})$$

in which $\mathbf{a}$ is again the appropriate lattice constant; i.e.,

$$\psi_k(\mathbf{r}) = (\exp i\mathbf{k} \cdot \mathbf{r})u_k(\mathbf{r}) \tag{2.15}$$

The consequences of assuming that the electrons are nearly, but not completely, free may then be investigated by substituting the result (2.15), due to Bloch, into the wave equation and by assuming that the potential energy of the electron $V(\mathbf{r})$ is very much smaller than the total energy ε. Expressing $u_k(\mathbf{r})$ as a Fourier series, substituting in the wave equation, and making this assumption produces an expression for the energy which is identical to that given by Eq. (2.14) for free electrons. Examination reveals that the assumptions made about the relative insignificance of all but the leading coefficient in the Fourier series breaks down for values of $\mathbf{k}^2$ of the order of $(\mathbf{k}'_m)^2$, where

$$\mathbf{k}'_m = \mathbf{k} - (2\pi m/\mathbf{a})$$

m being an integer. In order to see what happens at these values of $\mathbf{k} = \pi m/\mathbf{a}$ it is necessary to express $u_k(\mathbf{r})$ in terms of the first two terms of the Fourier series representing it. Substituting this in the Schrödinger equation reveals abrupt changes in $\mathbf{k}$ at integral multiples of $\pi/\mathbf{a}$, as illustrated in Fig. 9. Energy states may therefore be thought of as existing in bands extending over particular ranges of energy, and it may be shown that the values of $\mathbf{k}$ at the energy discontinuities correspond to wavelengths λ which satisfy the familiar Bragg law of reflection,

$$l\lambda = 2a \sin \theta$$

where l is an integer and θ is the complement of the angle of incidence. These discontinuities correspond directly to surfaces in $\mathbf{k}$-space, the boundaries

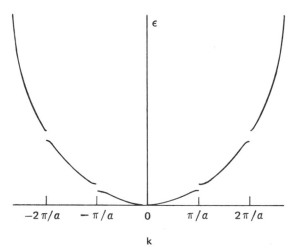

Fig. 9. The relationship between electron energy ε and wave vector **k**, illustrating the discontinuities produced by the periodic field of the lattice.

of which are defined vectors of length $m\pi/a$ and emerging from the origin, the Brillouin zones.

Having established that the energies of electrons in metals may increase quasicontinuously within discrete ranges or bands of energy, it will be useful to imagine next an atom stripped of its electrons, at the absolute zero of temperature. As the electrons are reintroduced, the lower energy states will fill up first, causing the increase in the radius of a sphere in momentum space. Since momentum is simply related to wave number, the growth of this sphere will be accompanied by the growth of a similar sphere within the first Brillouin zone in **k**-space, forming the Fermi surface. The growth of this sphere may be associated with a filling up of the lower energy states under the parabolic band shown in Fig. 7. As the sphere in **k**-space approaches the boundaries of the Brillouin zone, the number of energy states per unit energy range will begin to exceed the value predicted by the free-electron theory. After the sphere has touched the boundary of the zone it will become distorted from a sphere as it proceeds to fill the remainder of the zone, assuming a shape which is characteristic of the metal. This further filling will be accompanied by a fall in the electron distribution curve since the density of energy states within the remaining volume of the zone is diminishing. When the zone is completely filled the distribution curve would normally fall to zero and a finite increase in electron energy would occur before the filling of another band was possible. In the case of most metals, however, the lowest energy states of a succeeding zone are of lower energy than the highest energy states of the preceding zone. In this case the energy bands overlap and electrons would tend to enter the succeeding zone before completing the filling of the preceding zone. The resultant $v(\varepsilon)$–ε curve would in this case not fall to zero before all the electrons had gone into the second band; it might even show a subsidiary maximum. Detailed descriptions of the significance of Brillouin zones and Fermi surfaces have been given by, e.g., Ziman (1964).

In a detailed review of the specific heats of metals at low temperatures Parkinson (1958) has classified results for monovalent metals, divalent and other nontransition metals, the transition metals, superconductors, and rare earth metals. Summaries of this kind are helpful for the understanding of thermal expansion phenomena, the appreciation of limitations of the effective mass concept by pointing out discrepancies between calculated and observed values, and in assessing the relative quantitative importance of electron–phonon interaction processes (cf., Buckingham and Schafroth, 1954). The reader is directed to works of this nature and thence to original papers for detailed information on the behavior of individual metals. In the cases of metals which have overlapping electron energy bands it is natural to inquire about the extent to which particular electrons may be associated with particular bands. In a calculation based upon the assumption that the overlapping 3d and 4s bands of nickel are parabolic and that the electrons are distributed according to the collective electron expression, Wohlfarth (1948) showed that at temperatures above the absolute zero a temperature-dependent transfer of electrons should occur from the d band to the s band. Utilizing a scheme developed by Stoner (1939) and assuming that electrons might pass freely between the d and s bands, so that the number of holes in the d band would equal the number of electrons in the s band at all temperatures, Wohlfarth (1948) obtained a result which indicated that a transfer of electrons from the d band to the s band would be expected to accompany a rise in temperature. In a later paper on collective electron ferromagnetism (1949), he extended his treatment of the transfer effect to alloys of nickel and copper. Estimates of the extent of transfers such as these involve a knowledge of the shapes of the electron energy bands. Wohlfarth assumed parabolic bands, but it is doubtful whether this assumption is often valid, and attempts have been made to estimate band shapes from measurements of specific heats at low temperatures. The transition elements present a sequence to which attempts of this kind have been applied. Because of overlap between the 4d and 5s electron energy bands in palladium and between the 5d and 6s bands in platinum, these metals have formed the subjects of such attempts. Assuming that at the absolute zero of temperature all the electrons moved into the lowest available energy states, a calculation of the electronic heat coefficient from low-temperature specific heat measurements provided a measure of the density of states at the Fermi limit. Alloying with the appropriate element having an adjacent atomic number was then supposed to have increased or decreased the number of electrons in the outermost band, and to have produced an appropriate shift in energy of the density of states at the Fermi surface (e.g., Hoare and Yates, 1957; Dixon *et al.*, 1967; Budworth *et al.*, 1960). Calculations such as these assumed a rigid band model and neglected electron–phonon interaction. Detailed interpretations of results are not easy because of assumptions implicit in this model, the shapes of the bands, the number of holes in the overlapping *s* bands, and complications associated with the high concentration of one element in the other.

2.3. SPECIFIC HEAT ANOMALIES

The use of the word anomaly implies the acceptance of an established mode of behavior, and the two major contributions to the specific heat of a solid are indisputably those arising from the energies associated with the lattice and the electrons. Temperature-dependent changes in the energy content of solids resulting from, e.g., changes in crystal structure, changes in the mode of vibration, and magnetic ordering processes usually occur over relatively narrow ranges of temperature and may give rise to peaks which are superimposed upon an otherwise monotonic increase of specific heat with temperature. For the present purpose variations of this kind, involving ordering in coordinate space, will be classified as anomalies. Ordering processes in momentum space occur in transitions to the states of superfluidity and superconductivity, corresponding to which anomalies occur in the temperature variations of specific heat, but these will be omitted from the present considerations.

Considering first the case of a bodily movement of atoms, this will result in a spatial rearrangement, associated with which the energy adjustment involved will give rise to an anomaly in the otherwise steady rise of specific heat with temperature. Examples of order–disorder transformations showing this type of behavior are to be found among metallic alloys such as AuCu, $AuCu_3$, CuZn, CuPt, and AgZn, and also at the glass transition, examples of which may be seen in the works of S. S. Chang *et al.* (1967) on diethyl phthalate glasses and Adachi *et al.* (1968) on cyclohexanol. Anomalies might equally be expected in cases in which the structures of the first and last states are regular, e.g., in transformations from the body-centered cubic structure to the face-centered cubic structure in CsCl accompanying a rise of temperature in the region of 450°C, and associated with structural changes in the reverse direction accompanying increases of pressure to KF, RbF, RbCl, and CsF. In some cases more than one anomaly may be seen in the results for one substance. For example, Matsuo *et al.* (1968) have shown that sodium cyanide displays an order–disorder transition at approximately 172°K, followed by the onset of hindered rotation of the cyanide ion at approximately 288°K, associated with each of which transitions there is an anomaly in the specific heat curve.

The last-mentioned transition is an example of the manifestation of a further source of specific heat anomaly, the transformation of one mode of molecular motion to another. In the case of molecules in which relatively loose bonds provide the restraint of hindered rotations or torsional oscillations about a mean position, an increase of temperature may result in a reduction of this restraint, accompanying an increased separation of the constituents and an increase in the energy of the motions, which together result in a transition to complete molecular rotation. A transition of this kind occurs in methane at approximately 20°K, and similar effects occur in other molecular solids, e.g., hydrogen, deuterium, ethane, and hydrogen iodide, the finer details of which are not fully understood at the present time. Corresponding to such changes, λ-shaped peaks are again observed in the graphs of specific heat against temperature.

In the case of atoms or molecules which possess permanent magnetic moments, exchange interaction can overcome the random nature of the spins at sufficiently low temperatures. The spins may become ordered and parallel, as occurs in ferromagnetics below the Curie temperature. Alternatively, the spins may be aligned antiparallel, as occurs in antiferromagnetics below the Néel temperature. In substances such as β-Co(OH)$_2$ and Ni(OH)$_2$, which possess the CdI$_2$ structure and in which ferromagnetic coupling occurs between the metal ions within parallel layers, and antiferromagnetic ordering results between the layers, the Curie and Néel temperatures actually coincide (Sorai, 1967). Again, the antiparallelism may arise between spins of different magnitude, as occurs in ferrites and garnets. The main features of manifestations of magnetic ordering in specific heats are embodied in the Schottky specific heat, the nuclear specific heat, and cooperative phenomena.

If we have a physical system the energy of which is quantized so that it is composed of two levels separated by ΔE in energy, then at temperatures well below $\Delta E/k$ the higher energy level will be almost completely empty. At temperatures well in excess of $\Delta E/k$, on the other hand, this level will be almost fully populated. The additional energy required for the excitation as $T = \Delta E/k$ is approached will give rise to an additional contribution to the specific heat, which shows up as a peak on an otherwise steadily rising graph with temperature. This phenomenon was considered in some detail by Schottky (1922), who considered a more complex system than the one considered here, consisting of a number of energy levels. The energy levels necessary to display transitions of this type are caused by splitting resulting from magnetic interaction between the electronic magnetic dipole of a paramagnetic ion with the static electric field within the crystal lattice, resulting in $2s + 1$ orientations of the spin $s\hbar$. Interpretations of anomalies of this type may be directed toward determining the separations of the levels in energy and to giving information concerning the degeneracies of the levels. Manganese carbonate, α-nickel sulfate hexahydrate, ferric methylammonium sulfate, cerium ethylsulfate, and halides of iron, cobalt, and nickel are typical of substances which display this type of anomaly. When the nucleus of an atom possesses a magnetic moment, this may interact with the electron dipole moment to cause a further splitting, corresponding to which anomalies similar to Schottky anomalies may occur, but at lower temperatures, because of the smaller energy differences between levels. Examples of this phenomenon are provided by Co and by fluorides of Mn, Fe, Co, and Ni, and it has also been observed in the rare earth metals Sm, Tb, Dy, Ho, and Er. When the atoms or ions of a solid are relatively close in space, so that strong coupling occurs between them, it becomes more meaningful to speak in terms of the energy of the whole assembly, rather than of the energies of individual atoms in the matrix. Again the anomaly manifests itself as a peak in the specific heat curve, examples of which are provided by solid hydrogen and by the chloroiridates of sodium, potassium, and ammonium.

The magnetic origin of anomalies such as these has been brought out by work such as that of Fritz et al. (1967), who have shown how the magnetic field influences the Néel temperature and the magnitude of the heat capacity considered as a function of temperature in the case of $Mn(NH_4)_2(SO_4)_2 \cdot 6H_2O$. A useful summary of the various physical properties of solids which display anomalies in their variations with temperature upon transforming to the antiferromagnetic state has been given by Nagamiya et al. (1955), while Goodenough (1966) has reviewed the types of magnetic ordering which may result in anomalies. It should be emphasized that the foregoing remarks refer to the principal features only of these phenomena, and an exact application of these concepts to individual substances is sometimes complicated by additional effects, a summary of which has been given by Gopal (1966).

A further magnetic contribution to the heat capacity of some solids may arise from spin waves. Effects originating from this source do not result in peaks superimposed upon an otherwise smooth curve of specific heat against temperature. The phenomenon may be regarded as an anomaly in the sense that it is uncommon, and mention of it is made because of recent ideas concerning the related influence of spin waves upon thermal expansion, which will be mentioned later. In the case of metals at low temperatures a term proportional to $T^{3/2}$ is to be expected to represent this effect, giving

$$C_V = \gamma_e T + b T^3 + \delta T^{3/2}$$

γ_e, b, and δ being constants, in which the first two terms represent the contributions from the electrons and the lattice, respectively, and unambiguous recognition of the magnetic term calls for very high experimental precision. In ferrimagnets, which are electrical insulators, the low-temperature expression for the specific heat takes the form

$$C_V = b T^3 + \delta T^{3/2}$$

and a separation of terms at low temperatures is much easier. Examples of this behavior are provided by magnetite, garnets, ferrites, and ferromagnetic insulators, and a particularly beautiful set of results has been produced for yttrium iron garnet by Edmonds and Petersen (1959).

As a final example of anomalies, mention may be made of λ-type peaks in specific heat curves resulting from the ferroelectric ordering which accompanies the onset of ferroelectricity in compounds such as potassium dihydrogen phosphate. In fact, quite a wide range of possible abrupt or relatively abrupt physical changes within solids may occur with change of temperature, corresponding to which specific heat anomalies might be expected. The principal features of the major contributions to this class of phenomena have been summarized briefly because of the occurrence of corresponding anomalies in the temperature variation of thermal expansion, though the details in all of the individual cases are by no means fully understood.

2.4. THE SPECIFIC HEAT OF DISORDERED SOLIDS

No detailed mention has yet been made about the effect of disorder upon the specific heat of a solid. We may look at two well-known types of solid displaying this characteristic as typical examples of this class; glasses and polymers.

2.4.1. Glasses

In spite of other complications, the lack of long-range order in glasses results in macroscopic isotropy, which simplifies the study of some of the physical properties. Glasses and diamond-structure solids have in common a relatively open structure, as shown in Fig. 25, and we may look at the well-known θ–T curve of germanium as being fairly representative of this type of solid. This contains a deep minimum (see Flubacher *et al.*, 1959*a*), which is associated with a low-lying peak in the frequency distribution, which in turn is attributed to high dispersion in the transverse acoustic branches of the spectrum. Analysis of the heat capacity data allows the position and approximate weight of the peak to be determined. Because of its complexity, it is not possible to determine detailed information about the high-frequency part of the spectrum, although averages of the frequency distribution, contained in the moments and their volume variation, may be determined with the aid of the quasiharmonic approximation just as they can for crystalline solids. A return to these concepts will be made later.

The low-frequency peak is particularly interesting in the present context because it leads to an illustration of the application of thermal expansion in discriminating between possible explanations of the origin of unusual specific heat behavior. Assuming that the harmonic approximation holds at the lowest temperatures, we should expect the distribution function $f(\nu)$ to vary with frequency ν according to the equation

$$f(\nu) = \alpha \nu^2 + \beta \nu^4 + \gamma \nu^6 + \cdots$$

in which $f(\nu)$ is the number of normal modes of vibration per unit frequency range, which corresponds to a variation of the specific heat with temperature according to the equation

$$C_V = aT^3 + bT^5 + cT^7 + \cdots$$

in which α, a, β, b, γ, c, ... are constants. If this were true, a graph of C_P/T^3 versus T^2 would be expected to approach linearity as $T \to 0$ for glasses as it does for, e.g., alkali halides. In fact, a large peak has been found by Flubacher *et al.* (1959*b*) below approximately $\theta_0^C/30$, corresponding to a peak in the vibrational frequency spectrum, although this contains only a small fraction of the total number of modes. This characteristic is not restricted to the disordered state, however, since the crystalline modifications of both silica and sodium tetraborate display qualitatively similar characteristics (Leadbetter, 1968*a*), and any differences between the vibrational spectra of the crystalline and disordered modifications of the same compound appear to be due mainly to differences of density. A factor contributing to the anomalously large low-temperature heat capacity of glasses is considered to be the existence of localized modes of very low frequency associated with network defects. Discontinuities in the specific heat versus temperature curves of glasses associated with structural changes accompanying the glass transition were mentioned in Section 2.3. A fuller description of the temperature variation of the specific heats of glass in the neighborhood of the transition, including the influence of cooling rate, has been given by Stevels (1962).

Returning to a consideration of the specific heat of glass at temperatures below the glass transition, some of the major findings concerning the influences of neutron irradiation and fictive temperature are summarized in Figs. 10 and 11. These may be summarized as follows:

(a) There is an anomaly in the low-temperature specific heat of vitreous silica.

(b) The magnitude of this anomaly is reduced by raising the fictive temperature.

(c) The magnitude is substantially reduced by neutron irradiation except at the lowest temperatures, where the effect of irradiation is only slight.

(d) There is no anomaly in the low-temperature heat capacity of quartz.

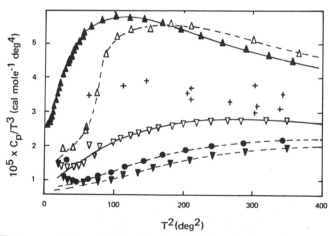

Fig. 10.   The temperature variation of the specific heats of various forms of silica, showing the influence of neutron irradiation (after Leadbetter and Morrison, 1963): ▲, vitreous silica; +, vitreous silica irradiated with $>5 \times 10^{19}$ neutrons cm^{-2}; ▼, quartz; ●, quartz irradiated with 2.5×10^{19} neutrons cm^{-2}; ▽, quartz irradiated with 7.7×10^{19} neutrons cm^{-2}; and △, cristobalite.

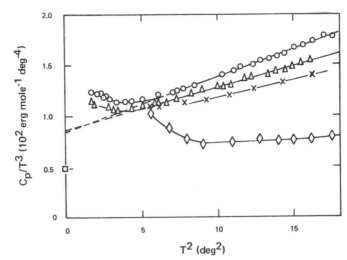

Fig. 11. The temperature variation of the specific heat of vitreous silica, which has been given different fictive temperatures (after White and Birch, 1965): ○, Vitreosil (1000°C); △, Vitreosil (1400°C); ×, Flubacher *et al.* (1959*b*); ◇, Spectrosil (irradiated); □, θ_0 (elastic).

(e) An anomaly is introduced into the low-temperature heat capacity of quartz by neutron irradiation.

Various explanations of this excess specific heat were suggested:

(a) An elongated Si-O-Si bond with two equilibrium positions for the bridging oxygen atom in the bond leads to a system of split energy levels, the separation of the lowest pair of which is consistent with a Schottky anomaly of the magnitude observed in fused silica. Between 10 and 20% of elongated bonds would explain the anomaly observed.

(b) An explanation based upon transverse vibrations of the oxygen atoms between different possible equilibrium positions was suggested. This required fewer defect bonds than the explanation proposed above.

(c) The presence of six-membered rings of Si–O in the disordered structure could conceivably give rise to vibrational modes of very low frequency.

Clark and Strakna (1962) showed that the frequencies associated with the specific heat anomaly were consistent with the observed low-frequency Raman spectrum and with an observed large low-temperature ultrasonic attenuation peak. Incidentally, these workers also observed that the specific heat of fast-neutron-irradiated fused silica was substantially lower than that of the unirradiated starting material between 7 and 25°K, confirmed by the later work of Leadbetter and Morrison (1963). Flubacher *et al.* (1959*b*) had earlier found correlation between velocities of transverse and longitudinal waves calculated from their observations of Brillouin spectra of vitreous silica and values measured acoustically. They also investigated the Raman spectrum, and concluded that both sets of spectroscopic observations were quantitatively consistent with the low-temperature heat capacity. It appears as though these various properties are all consistent with low-frequency modes arising from either a highly dispersive acoustic branch or a very-low-frequency optical branch of the spectrum. The similarity of the low-temperature heat capacities of cristobalite and vitreous silica when plotted on a reduced temperature scale, together with the observation that the radiation-induced reduction in the heat capacity of vitreous silica decreases with fall of temperature, strongly suggests that the low-frequency modes arise from two causes. The modes of lowest frequency are likely to be localized vibrations associated with structural defects which are not affected significantly by neutron irradiation, whereas the modes of higher frequency appear to arise from some source which is strongly affected by neutron irradiation. In fact, it will be seen later from thermal expansion measurements that the latter vibrations are also influenced markedly by network-filling additives. The observations suggest that a large number of the structural defects in vitreous silica are eliminated either by raising the fictive temperature or by irradiating with fast neutrons, in some form of annealing process, whereas neutron radiation appears to introduce disorder into quartz.

Before leaving these observations it is worth noting the virtue of changing only one variable at a time in attempting to explore the influence of factors controlling a physical property. A combination of the work of Flubacher et al. (1959b) with earlier unpublished work of Westrum led to the conclusion that an increase in the fictive temperature of vitreous silica gave rise to an increase in the magnitude of the anomalously large low-temperature specific heat. The later work of Leadbetter and Morrison (1963) showed more convincingly that the reverse was actually the case, the earlier, erroneous result probably having arisen either from differences in impurity contents or unknown differences in manufacturing conditions, or both.

In concluding this section it may be noted that although the detailed vibrational frequency spectra of glasses are extremely complex, and that detailed determinations cannot be made from the direct inversion of heat capacity data, the spectra of vitreous silica, germania, and beryllium fluoride have been computed by Bell et al. (1968) and are in good agreement with observed bands in the infrared and Raman spectra.

2.4.2. Polymers

For both scientific and technological reasons interest in the specific heats of polymers has grown considerably in recent years. Stockmayer and Hecht (1953) calculated the frequency spectrum for the simple model of a large crystal composed of long, parallel polymer chains. The model assumed that CH_2 or other groups in the chain vibrated as units and that there were strong primary bonds between the units and weak interactions between adjacent chains. Starkweather (1960) indicated that this model could only be expected to represent the simplest polymeric structures, and these only at the lowest temperatures. This author showed that the model might be made to fit available calorimetric data for crystalline polyethylene between approximately 20 and 150°K and polytetrafluoroethylene between approximately 15 and 75°K, while at high temperatures the model broke down. Warfield and Petree (1962) attempted to fit the model to amorphous polymethylmethacrylate in the approximate temperature range 50–250°K with moderate success, and polystyrene in the approximate range 40–200°K with only limited success. Gotlib and Sochava (1963) criticized the model of Stockmayer and Hecht as being too coarse to permit a reasonable comparison of experimental and theoretical data, and they calculated the heat capacity of polyethylene and polytetrafluoroethylene by using the values of force constants obtained from infrared spectra, obtaining reasonably good agreement for polyethylene between 90 and 180°K and for teflon between 50 and 200°K, in which the contributions from the skeletal and side group vibrations were suitably weighted to fit the observations with which the results of the calculations were compared.

More recent measurements have increased the ranges of data for this type of solid, in terms of available molecule type, temperature range, and the influence of radiation, which permit the consideration of refinements to the broad pattern of vibrational behavior, which is now fairly well established. For example, Reese *et al.* (1968) have shown how exposure to an 80-MeV electron beam reduced the low-temperature heat capacity of polystyrene by approximately 25%. This result is qualitatively similar to those mentioned earlier in connection with the neutron irradiation of glass, and it has been associated with a reduction of the excess heat capacity associated with low-frequency modes of vibration. The lack of data on the elastic and dilatometric properties of polymers leaves a gap in the knowledge which could be deduced from these two properties and the specific heat taken in association. This concerns the volume variation of the frequencies of the vibrations. Also, there has been a tendency to estimate heat capacities at the lowest temperatures in preference to measuring them. This trend is being revised, however, though there remains much valuable work to be performed in this fertile field, both on the direct measurement of specific heats and in the closely related fields of thermal expansion and elastic constants.

2.5. SURFACE SPECIFIC HEATS

In the substances considered so far, the ratio of surface area to volume has been tacitly ignored, and the propagation of longitudinal and transverse waves through an effectively infinite medium was considered in the Debye theory of specific heats. In the case of finely divided powders, however, account of surface waves should be included. By analogy with the earlier derivation, we may expect the low-temperature expression for the number of frequencies in the frequency range v to $v + dv$ associated with material of volume V and surface area $\mathscr{S}$, i.e., $f(v)\,dv$, to be augmented by a term to allow for the existence of surface waves. Thus, we may write

$$f(v)\,dv = AVv^2\,dv + B\mathscr{S}v\,dv$$

in which A and B are constants, corresponding to which the expression for the specific heat is

$$C_V = A'VT^3 + B'\mathscr{S}T^2$$

A' and B' being constants.

In an investigation of the occurrence of particle size effects, Dugdale et al. (1954) measured the heat capacity of four samples of titanium dioxide in the temperature range 12–270°K. The samples consisted of high-purity material having specific surfaces ranging between 8.5 and 100 m² g⁻¹. No evidence of particle size effects was detected below 50°K, but above this temperature the specific heat of the finer material increased more rapidly with temperature than did that of the coarse material. Because of the reduced temperatures at which these pronounced effects became evident, they were attributed to the optical modes rather than to the acoustic modes of vibration in the solid. Earlier, Montroll (1950) had drawn attention to an omission in the customary process of counting the normal modes of vibration, and he derived a corresponding correction term for the Debye spectrum:

$$f(v) = (\pi/2)\mathscr{S}[(2/c_t^2) + (1/c_l^2)]v$$

proportional to the area $\mathscr{S}$ of the solid. In applying his ideas, however, he took an idealized model having perfectly reflecting boundary faces. Later

authors attempted to take some account of more realistic boundary conditions. For example, Dupuis *et al.* (1960) acknowledged that in the cases of
both a free surface and a clamped surface, an incident longitudinal wave
would be followed by a transverse component as well as a longitudinal
component in the reflected wave. Their treatment resulted in a term in the
expression for the specific heat which was proportional to both the surface
area and to T^2. A similar treatment of the problem has been given by
Stratton (1953, 1962). Although their prediction was bigger than that of
Montroll for the case of a free surface, i.e., the case more closely approxi-
mating physical reality, it was still somewhat lower than experimental results
for sodium chloride powders having specific surfaces of 38 m^2 g^{-1} and
59 m^2 g^{-1}. Following a number of suggested explanations of the temperature dependences of the low-temperature specific heats of various types
of graphite, Flubacher *et al.* (1960*b*) showed that inconsistencies resulting
from the various approaches were removed if provision was made for a
particle size effect. In particular, they found that all the results could be
represented in the limiting case of low temperatures by the equation

$$C_V = 0.3 \times 10^{-5}T + (6.2_7 \pm 0.0_6) \times 10^{-6}T^3 + bT^2 \text{ cal (g-atom)}^{-1} \text{ deg}^{-1}$$

in which the first, second, and third terms on the right-hand side represent
the electronic, lattice, and surface contributions to the specific heat, respectively.

   Following the development of interest in the physics of thin films,
Corciovei and Motoc (1963) considered the thermal vibrations in such
bodies, and the specific heat to which these would give rise. Their treatment
is highly mathematical, and the original work should be consulted for details
of the derivation of an expression for the low-temperature specific heat
which is a function of the number of atomic layers. As this number tends
toward very small values, the temperature dependence tends toward the
T^2 form; as it tends to large values, we get the familiar T^3 form. The theory
also shows that the effect of the substrate upon which the film would normally be deposited would be to reduce the heat capacity of the film because
of the binding force between the two over their common surface. At high
temperatures we get the required independence of temperature. Unfortunately, there do not appear to be any results available for the heat capacities
of thin films with which the predictions of the theory may be compared at
the present time.

   Maradudin and Wallis (1966) have performed a lattice-dynamical calculation, treating the free bounding surfaces of the crystal as perturbations

of an unperturbated crystal in which the atomic displacements satisfy the cyclic boundary condition. The theory has been applied to a nearest- and next-nearest-neighbor central-force model of a simple cubic crystal, the force constants of which were chosen to give elastic isotropy in the long-wavelength limit. This atomic approach produced a result in agreement with that emerging from the elasticity approach of Dupuis *et al.*

Sorai (1967) has measured the specific heats of three samples of $Ni(OH)_2$ having specific surfaces extending from approximately 6 to 320 m² g⁻¹. This compound is particularly interesting because of a magnetic transition, which results in a specific heat anomaly with a maximum in the region of 24°K. Sorai observed that at temperatures well above the anomaly, in the vicinity of 100°K in fact, the specific heats of the different specimens increased with diminution of particle size, and that the temperature variations were essentially parallel at these temperatures. The influence of particle size effect on magnitude accorded with earlier observations, though the parallelism was not in keeping with the earlier findings by Dugdale *et al.* (1954) on titanium dioxide. Comparing his results with those of earlier workers on NaCl, BeO, and MgO, Sorai observed that the excess specific heat resulting from size effects was roughly proportional to the surface area per unit mass of the particles. In the region of the excess specific heat arising from magnetic interaction effects, however, he observed that the magnitude of the magnetic contribution was reduced by reducing the particle size, in contrast to the effect on the lattice contribution at higher temperatures. Also, the temperature at which the maximum occurred was reduced from 24.8 to 23.0°K as the particle size was reduced over the range mentioned earlier.

In attempting to summarize this very inadequate mention of surface effects, one may conclude:

(a) Experiments on finely divided powders have established the existence of a surface contribution to the heat capacity of a solid, though the ranges of reduced temperature in which the effects have been reported contain a considerable variation.

(b) Theoretical treatments of surface specific heats in small particles differ in detail, but appear to agree on a term in the expression for the heat capacity at low temperatures which is proportional to both the surface area and to T^2.

(c) A theoretical treatment of the subject applied specifically to thin films has arrived at similar conclusions, apart from modifications to allow for the presence of the supporting substrate.

(d) There is a distinct shortage of quantitative experimental specific heat data required to provide the means of performing rigorous tests of the various theories. This need is particularly acute in the case of thin films.

Chapter 3

Elastic Properties of Solids

3.1. EARLY EQUATIONS OF STATE

It will be appropriate to introduce the idea of the interrelationship of of specific heat, elastic constants, and thermal expansion before moving to a consideration of the two last-named phenomena in more detail. This may be effected conveniently by a brief consideration of early equations of state, which paved the way to a more realistic treatment of the volume variation of the frequencies of lattice vibrations, which treatment is considered in more detail in a later chapter.

Debye (1913) followed his specific heat theory by accounting for volume changes with temperature in terms of an equation of state. Grüneisen (1926) also considered the vibrational frequencies to be volume-dependent and derived an equation of state which was consistent with that of Debye. By differentiating the equation defining the Helmholtz free energy F,

$$F = U - TS$$

in which U represents the total internal energy of the assembly, and substituting from the first law of thermodynamics

$$T \, dS = dU + P \, dV$$

we may show that

$$P = -(\partial F / \partial V)_T \tag{3.1}$$

Writing F in terms of T and V,

$$F = U_0 + F_{\mathrm{D}}(T, V) \tag{3.2}$$

where U_0 is the internal energy at 0°K and $F_D(T, V)$ is the contribution to the free energy arising from the temperature-dependent lattice vibrations in the Debye approximation. From (3.1) and (3.2),

$$P = -(\partial U_0/\partial V) - (\partial F_D/\partial V)_T$$

which we may write in the form

$$P = -(\partial U_0/\partial V) - (\partial F_D/\partial \theta)_T(d\theta/dV)_T \qquad (3.3)$$

Substituting $x = h\nu/kT$ and $\theta = h\nu_D/k$ in Eq. (2.5), we get

$$U_D = 9NkT(T/\theta)^3 \int_0^{\theta/T} [x^3/(e^x - 1)]\, dx$$

for the internal energy U_D in the Debye approximation, i.e., the temperature-dependent part of the internal energy may be expressed as the product of T and a function of θ/T. By definition, $F_D(T, V)$ must be of the same form as U_D, i.e.,

$$F_D = T \cdot f(\theta/T) \qquad (3.4)$$

where $f(\theta/T)$ is a function of θ/T. Thus,

$$\frac{\partial F_D}{\partial \theta} = \frac{\partial}{\partial \theta}\left[Tf\left(\frac{\theta}{T}\right)\right] = T\frac{\partial[f(\theta/T)]}{\partial(\theta/T)} \cdot \frac{d(\theta/T)}{d\theta}$$
$$= \frac{\partial[f(\theta/T)]}{\partial(\theta/T)} \qquad (3.5)$$

Also,

$$\frac{\partial(F_D/T)}{\partial(1/T)} = \frac{\partial[f(\theta/T)]}{\partial(1/T)} = \frac{\partial[f(\theta/T)]}{\partial(\theta/T)} \cdot \frac{d(\theta/T)}{d(1/T)}$$
$$= \theta\,\frac{\partial F_D}{\partial \theta} \qquad \text{[from (3.5)]} \qquad (3.6)$$

But

$$\frac{\partial(F_D/T)}{\partial(1/T)} = U_D \qquad (3.7)$$

Thus, from (3.6) and (3.7),

$$\partial F_D/\partial \theta = U_D/\theta$$

Substituting this result in (3.3) gives

$$P = -\frac{\partial U_0}{\partial V} - \frac{U_D}{\theta}\left(\frac{\partial \theta}{\partial V}\right)_T = -\frac{\partial U_0}{\partial V} - \frac{U_D}{V}\left[\frac{V}{\theta}\left(\frac{\partial \theta}{\partial V}\right)_T\right]$$

This equation, known as the Debye equation of state, is usually written in the form

$$P = -(\partial U_0/\partial V) + \gamma(U_D/V) \qquad (3.8)$$

where

$$\gamma = -(V/\theta)(\partial\theta/\partial V)_T = -d(\ln \theta)/d(\ln V) \qquad (3.9)$$

In accordance with Debye's theory, θ is independent of temperature and therefore γ, the Grüneisen constant as it was called, should also be independent of temperature. Continuing in the spirit of the Debye theory, we may relate γ to physically measurable quantities by differentiating Eq. (3.8) with respect to temperature at constant volume, i.e.,

$$(\partial P/\partial T)_V = \gamma(C_V/V) \qquad (3.10)$$

But

$$(\partial P/\partial T)_V = -(\partial V/\partial T)_P(\partial P/\partial V)_T \qquad (3.11)$$

Writing the volume coefficient of thermal expansion

$$\beta = (1/V)(\partial V/\partial T)_P$$

and the isothermal bulk modulus of elasticity

$$K_T = -V(\partial P/\partial V)_T$$

and substituting these results in Eq. (3.10) gives

$$\gamma = \beta V K_T/C_V \qquad (3.12)$$

From elementary thermodynamics one may show that this may be written in the alternative form

$$\gamma = \beta V K_S/C_P \qquad (3.13)$$

At the time at which these equations were being developed, K_T was taken to be independent of temperature, and this led directly to the conclusion that $\beta \propto C_V$ to a good approximation, which was known as Grüneisen's rule or law. Experiment shows that Grüneisen's law is only true for the majority of familiar solids at intermediate and higher temperatures, and to this extent it is to be regarded as a first approximation. We shall return to a more detailed consideration of the Grüneisen parameter and its temperature variation later. Meanwhile we shall look briefly at another experimentally accessible term in Eqs. (3.12) and (3.13), the bulk modulus of elasticity.

3.2. FORMAL REPRESENTATION OF STRESS AND STRAIN

As the temperature of a body is increased, the thermal motion of one atom will affect the motion of its neighbors, resulting in the manifestation of anharmonic effects. Variations of elastic moduli with temperature are therefore to be expected and do, in fact, occur, although they are frequently comparatively small. The relative change in the dimensions of a body produced by forces acting upon it is termed a strain. The force producing the strain, expressed in terms of its magnitude per unit area, is called the stress. In terms of stress and strain Hooke's law, which is applicable to a wide range of solids, may be expressed by stating that stress is proportional to strain for small deformations. For such isotropic solids we may describe the well-known moduli of elasticity, Young's modulus Y, bulk modulus K, and rigidity or shear modulus n, by reference to Fig. 12. Referring to Fig. 12(a),

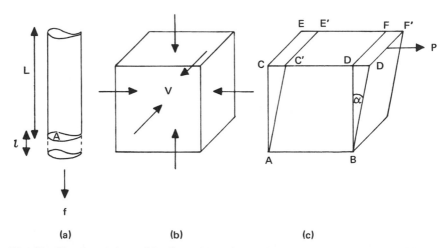

(a)   (b)   (c)

Fig. 12. Representation of bodies subjected to: (a) longitudinal stress, in which the force f produces an extension l in a length L of material of cross-sectional area A, giving Young's modulus $Y = (f/A)/(l/L)$; (b) uniform volume compression, in which the applied pressure P applied to volume V causes a dilatation v, leading to the bulk modulus $K = -P/(v/V)$; and (c) tangential stress, in which a force of magnitude P per unit area acting over the surface CF results in a displacement through the angle α to $C'F'$, from which the modulus of rigidity may be defined as $n = P/\alpha$.

we may define

$$Y = \frac{\text{stress}}{\text{strain}} = \frac{f/A}{l/L}$$

In Fig. 12(b) a uniform compressional force of magnitude P per unit area acting uniformly over the surface of the volume V may be supposed to produce a decrease of volume v, from which

$$K = \frac{\text{stress}}{\text{strain}} = \frac{P}{v/V}$$

Figure 12(c) depicts a block subjected to a tangential force per unit area P acting over the surface $CDFE$, which is displaced to $C'D'F'E'$ as a result. The strain may be measured by the displacement angle θ, allowing the definition of the rigidity modulus (or shear modulus)

$$n = \frac{\text{stress}}{\text{strain}} = \frac{P}{\theta}$$

It may be shown fairly easily that the three moduli are related by the well-known equation

$$\frac{3}{n} + \frac{1}{K} = \frac{9}{Y} \tag{3.14}$$

to a very good approximation, from which it will be seen that a knowledge of any two of the three moduli of elasticity allows the third to be calculated. Another quantity which is frequently used in solid-state elasticity theory is Poisson's ratio σ, defined as the ratio of lateral strain, measured by the decrease of width per unit width, to the longitudinal strain. This may be related to the moduli of elasticity by means of Eqs. (3.14) and (3.15), where

$$\sigma = (Y/2n) - 1 \tag{3.15}$$

What we have said so far refers to isotropic bodies, but a number of single crystals of elements and compounds of great interest are anisotropic. It is necessary, therefore, to consider the stresses and strains in particular directions with respect to the orientations of well-ordered crystals.

3.2.1. Components of Stress

Retaining our definition of stress as the force per unit area acting in a solid, we now adopt a system of notation in which a capital letter denotes the direction in which the force acts and a subscript identifies the normal

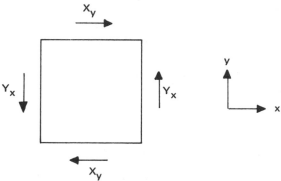

Fig. 13.   The stresses in a two-dimensional body.

to the plane on which the force acts. Referring to Fig. 13, which shows two of the three dimensions of a body, we induce that the possible stresses are X_x, X_y, X_z, Y_x, Y_y, Y_z, Z_x, Z_y, and Z_z. From Fig. 13 it may be seen that if the body is to be in equilibrium i.e., if it is not to rotate, $X_y = Y_x$, and in the three-dimensional case $Y_z = Z_y$ and $Z_x = X_z$ also. Thus the nine independent stress components are reduced to six for a solid in equilibrium: X_x, Y_y, Z_z, Y_z, Z_x, and X_y.

3.2.2. Components of Strain

The uniform strain in the body may be resolved similarly into six components. In order to have a single system of notation to include extension strains and shear strains, the shear strains are expressed in terms of extension strains as follows. Using the symbol e for extension strain, two subscripts are added giving the directions perpendicular to two planes separated by unit distance, the relative displacements of which are of magnitude e. In the case of displacements normal to orthogonal x, y, and z axes, for example, the strains are straightforward extension strains denoted by e_{xx}, e_{yy}, and e_{zz}, respectively. The shear strains are expressed in terms of the relative tangential displacement of the planes, unit distance apart. For example, e_{xy} is the relative displacement of planes perpendicular to the x and y axes, respectively. With this notation

$$e_{xy} = e_{yx}, \qquad e_{yz} = e_{zy}, \qquad \text{and} \qquad e_{zx} = e_{xz}$$

leaving us with the strains

$$e_{xx}, \quad e_{yy}, \quad e_{zz}, \quad e_{yz}, \quad e_{zx}, \quad \text{and} \quad e_{xy}$$

Applying Hooke's law, we may now write the strains e_{xx}, etc. as linear functions of the stresses X_x, etc. in the form

$$e_{xx} = S_{11}X_x + S_{12}Y_y + S_{13}Z_z + S_{14}Y_z + S_{15}Z_x + S_{16}X_y$$
$$e_{yy} = S_{21}X_x + S_{22}Y_y + S_{23}Z_z + S_{24}Y_z + S_{25}Z_x + S_{26}X_y$$
$$e_{zz} = S_{31}X_x + S_{32}Y_y + S_{33}Z_z + S_{34}Y_z + S_{35}Z_x + S_{36}X_y$$
$$e_{yz} = S_{41}X_x + S_{42}Y_y + S_{43}Z_z + S_{44}Y_z + S_{45}Z_x + S_{46}X_y$$
$$e_{zx} = S_{51}X_x + S_{52}Y_y + S_{53}Z_z + S_{54}Y_z + S_{55}Z_x + S_{56}X_y$$
$$e_{xy} = S_{61}X_x + S_{62}Y_y + S_{63}Z_z + S_{64}Y_z + S_{65}Z_x + S_{66}X_y$$

$$(3.16)$$

where S_{11}, S_{12}, etc. are called the "elastic compliance constants." Similarly, we may express the stress components as linear functions of the strain components:

$$X_x = c_{11}e_{xx} + c_{12}e_{yy} + c_{13}e_{zz} + c_{14}e_{yz} + c_{15}e_{zx} + c_{16}e_{xy}$$
$$Y_y = c_{21}e_{xx} + c_{22}e_{yy} + c_{23}e_{zz} + c_{24}e_{yz} + c_{25}e_{zx} + c_{26}e_{xy}$$
$$Z_z = c_{31}e_{xx} + c_{32}e_{yy} + c_{33}e_{zz} + c_{34}e_{yz} + c_{35}e_{zx} + c_{36}e_{xy}$$
$$Y_z = c_{41}e_{xx} + c_{42}e_{yy} + c_{43}e_{zz} + c_{44}e_{yz} + c_{45}e_{zx} + c_{46}e_{xy}$$
$$Z_x = c_{51}e_{xx} + c_{52}e_{yy} + c_{53}e_{zz} + c_{54}e_{yz} + c_{55}e_{zx} + c_{56}e_{xy}$$
$$X_y = c_{61}e_{xx} + c_{62}e_{yy} + c_{63}e_{zz} + c_{64}e_{yz} + c_{65}e_{zx} + c_{66}e_{xy}$$

$$(3.17)$$

where c_{11}, c_{12}, etc. are called the "elastic stiffness constants."

Consider now a cube of side L, one corner of which coincides with the origin of coordinate axes x, y, and z. Subjecting the cube to stresses X_x, Y_y, Z_z, Y_z, Z_x, and X_y will produce the corresponding strains δe_{xx}, δe_{yy}, δe_{zz}, δe_{yz}, δe_{zx}, and δe_{xy}, which in turn will result in the expenditure of energy of amount

$$\delta W = L^3(X_x\, \delta e_{xx} + Y_y\, \delta e_{yy} + Z_z\, \delta e_{zz} + Y_z\, \delta e_{yz} + Z_x\, \delta e_{zx} + X_y\, \delta e_{xy})$$

The amount of energy stored per unit volume is thus

$$\delta U = X_x\, \delta e_{xx} + Y_y\, \delta e_{yy} + Z_z\, \delta e_{zz} + Y_z\, \delta e_{yz} + Z_x\, \delta e_{zx} + X_y\, \delta e_{xy} \quad (3.18)$$

It may be seen from Eq. (3.18) that $X_x = \partial U/\partial e_{xx}$ and $Y_y = \partial U/\partial e_{yy}$, from which it is clear that $\partial X_x/\partial e_{yy} = \partial Y_y/\partial e_{xx}$. Substituting this result into Eq. (3.17) yields the result $c_{12} = c_{21}$. Extending this procedure leads to the general result

$$c_{ij} = c_{ji}$$

from which it follows that the number of independent elastic stiffness constants is reduced from 36 to 21. By taking account of the symmetry elements possessed by various crystal structures, the number of independent elastic stiffness and compliance constants may be reduced still further. For example, in the simplest case of all, that of cubic crystals, there are only three of each. These are related by the equations

$$c_{11} = (s_{11} + s_{12})/(s_{11} - s_{12})(s_{11} + 2s_{12})$$
$$c_{12} = -s_{12}/(s_{11} - s_{12})(s_{11} + 2s_{12})$$
$$c_{44} = 1/s_{44}$$
$$s_{11} = (c_{11} + c_{12})/(c_{11} - c_{12})(c_{11} + 2c_{12})$$
$$s_{12} = -c_{12}/(c_{11} - c_{12})(c_{11} + 2c_{12})$$
$$s_{44} = 1/c_{44}$$

3.3. MEASUREMENTS OF MODULI OF ELASTICITY

The growth of theoretical interest in the physics of crystals has led to the need for a knowledge of the moduli of elasticity over a wide range of temperature, particularly at low temperatures. The restriction on specimen size caused by this requirement, the availability of many single crystals in the form of pieces having dimensions of a few millimeters only, and the anisotropy of many crystals have favored the development of acoustic methods of measuring elastic constants. In the case of cubic crystals we have seen that there are only three elastic stiffness constants to be measured, c_{11}, c_{12}, and c_{44}, from two of which, incidentally, the bulk modulus may be calculated directly as $K = (c_{11} + 2c_{12})/3$. c_{11}, c_{12}, and c_{44} may be derived conveniently from measurements of the velocities of three sound waves: a longitudinal wave traveling in the [100] direction with velocity $(c_{11}/\varrho)^{1/2}$, where ϱ is the density of the crystal, a shear wave of velocity $(c_{44}/\varrho)^{1/2}$ traveling in the same direction, and a shear wave moving with velocity $[(c_{11} - c_{12})/2\varrho]^{1/2}$ in the [110] direction, having particle motion polarized perpendicular to the [001] direction. As alternatives, one may measure the velocity of a shear wave propagated in the [110] direction with particle motion polarized parallel to the [001] direction, given by $(c_{44}/\varrho)^{1/2}$, or the velocity of a longitudinal wave moving in the [110] direction, given by $[(c_{11} + c_{12} + 2c_{44})/2\varrho]^{1/2}$. This is the simplest case of all, and the number of measurements necessary increases with the complexity of the crystal.

Experimentally, the technique consists in attaching a quartz transducer to one face of a crystal which has first been cut in order that the ultrasonic wave generated by the vibrating transducer will travel in the required

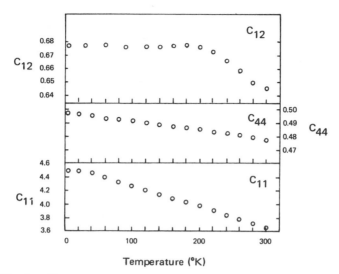

Fig. 14. Elastic stiffness constants of rubidium chloride in units of 10^{11} dyn cm^{-2} as functions of temperature (after Marshall *et al.* 1967).

direction and mode. It is customary to reflect the pulse or wave from the rear face of the crystal, and to measure the time between generation and receipt electronically. Among the circuits lending themselves to the very precise measurement of transit times may be mentioned the "sing-around" system of Forgacs (1958), which permits periods of the order of 10^{-4} sec to be measured to a precision of $\pm 10^{-9}$ sec. The solids to which the ultrasonic method has been applied in determining elastic constants include solidified rare gases, simple ionic solids, semiconductors, metals, and alloys (e.g., Keeler, 1969; Gerlich, 1964*a*,*b*; McSkimin and Andreatch, 1963; Belhami *et al.*, 1966). Perhaps the greatest volume of work has been performed on compounds characterized by simple ionic bonding, among which the alkali halides figure prominently. It is not possible to do justice to all the work performed on these solids in this brief account, though the work of Marshall *et al.* (1967) on LiCl and RbCl may be taken as fairly typical. A graph of their results for RbCl is shown in Fig. 14.

3.4. FURTHER CONSIDERATIONS

From somewhat detailed considerations of energy in connection with the propagation of elastic waves in cubic crystals it may be shown that the equation

$$c_{11} - c_{12} = 2c_{44} \tag{3.19}$$

constitutes the condition for a crystal to be elastically isotropic, i.e., for waves of a particular type to travel in all directions with equal velocities. This condition leads naturally to the definition of an "anisotropy factor," which for cubic crystals takes the form

$$A = 2c_{44}/(c_{11} - c_{12}) \qquad (3.20)$$

If, in addition, three conditions are fulfilled, then it may be shown that a set of relations will exist between the elastic stiffness constants, known as the Cauchy relations. For these to hold it is necessary that (a) the forces between the atoms should act along lines joining their centers; (b) every atom must be at a center of inversion symmetry; and (c) the crystal should be completely unstrained. In the case of cubic crystals the relations between the elastic stiffness constants reduce to

$$c_{12} = c_{44} \qquad (3.21)$$

The requirement concerning central forces is not generally fulfilled by covalent solids or by metals. On the other hand, the conditions in ionic crystals do approximate to this ideal in some measure. In the event of complete conformity with Eq. (3.21), Eq. (3.19) would lead to $c_{11} = 3c_{44}$ and Eq. (3.20) would give $A = 1$. Experiment has shown that A increases with temperature, and Lewis et $al.$ (1967) have shown that this results in the lithium halides becoming more anisotropic and the sodium, potassium, and rubidium halides becoming less anisotropic as the temperature rises from $T = 0$. In general c_{11} is strongly dependent upon temperature in the face-centered cubic alkali halides, whereas c_{12} and c_{44} are only weakly temperature-dependent, and c_{11} is several times greater than c_{12} and c_{44}. In the body-centered cubic alkali halides the variation of c_{44} between 4.2 and 300°K is approximately three times that of c_{11}. Lewis et $al.$ have tabulated $\Delta = c_{12} - c_{44}$ at 300 and 4.2°K for 13 face-centered cubic alkali halides. With the exception of rubidium iodide, Δ increases with rise in temperature and the trend is for Δ to increase with the mass of the alkali ion. It is difficult to see a consistent pattern of behavior in the variation of Δ with mass of the halide ion. This may be because any such variation is masked by experimental uncertainty. This is not the only lattice-dynamical property of lithium halides, the temperature variation of which is different from that of the same property in the other face-centered cubic alkali halides. For example, Yates and Panter (1962) found a significant difference in the temperature variations of the Grüneisen parameters. In the case of the anisotropy factor Huntington (1958) has explained the change in sign in $(c_{11} - c_{12})/2 \gtrless c_{44}$

between the lithium halides and the others in terms of the closed-shell repulsive potential between adjacent alkali and halide ions, in the light of the relative sizes of the ions. Because of the small size of the lithium ions, the smallest separation of adjacent ions in lithium halides is between the halide ions in the [110] directions, and not between the alkali and halide ions in the [100] directions. For the face-centered cubic alkali halides the alkali ion has a large effect on the magnitude of the anisotropy, and the nature of the halide ion has more effect on the anisotropy as the mass of the alkali ion increases. Reinitz (1961) has suggested that these results may have their origin in size effects. This is particularly plausible in the case of the lithium halides, for which the anisotropy factors are almost identical to one another and very close to unity, since the lithium ions are much smaller than the halide ions and may fit into the available holes in the lattice. The sodium ions would be expected to produce relatively small separations of the halide ions, but the effect of alkali ion size would becomes progressively more marked for the potassium and rubidium halides. The anisotropy factors of the body-centered cubic alkali halides cesium chloride, bromide, and iodide are close to unity, and it is thought that this may arise from the increased number of nearest neighbors, tending to make the crystal more isotropic.

Reasonably good agreement has been found between the experimentally observed characteristic infrared resonance frequencies and those calculated by applying experimental values of the high- and low-frequency dielectric constants and the measured compressibilities to theoretical relationships connecting these quantities and based upon the Born–Huang theory of lattice polarization (see, e.g., Szigeti, 1950; Karo, 1959, 1960; Vallin *et al.*, 1964; Lewis *et al.*, 1967).

In Section 2.1 we saw that Debye's assumption concerning the continuous and elastic nature of solids became an increasingly good approximation as the temperature approached absolute zero, and that the temperature independence of the Debye characteristic temperature in the immediate vicinity of $T = 0$ provided testimony to the acceptability of the Debye model in this region. By averaging the reciprocals of the cubes of the transverse and longitudinal velocities of sound waves over all directions in the crystal it is possible to calculate a value for the Debye characteristic temperature of the solid. It has been shown by Barron and Klein (1962) and Feldman (1964) that in the limit of very low temperatures the value of θ calculated in this way, θ_0^{el}, should be identical with that derived from specific heat measurements, θ_0^C. Various methods of approximation have been formulated in attempting to reduce the work involved in this somewhat laborious task, notable among which are the tables of de Launay (1954, 1956*a*, 1959), which were designed to be applicable to classes of solids for which particular inequalities held between the elastic constants.

The low-temperature elastic constants of a crystal may be used to calculate the lattice energy of the crystal at $T = 0$. Assuming that the interaction energy ϕ_{ij} between two ions i and j may be represented by the sum of a Coulomb potential and a repulsive potential varying as r_{ij}^{-n}, where r_{ij} is the separation of the ions, ϕ_{ij} may be written in the form

$$\phi_{ij} = (A/r_{ij}^n) \pm (e^2/r_{ij}) \tag{3.22}$$

in which e is the electronic charge and A is a constant. Introducing the nearest-neighbor distance R and a new variable p_{ij} in the form

$$r_{ij} = p_{ij}R$$

we find

$$\phi_{ij} = (1/p_{ij}^n)(A/R^n) \pm (1/p_{ij})(e^2/R)$$

and

$$\phi = (AB_n/R^n) - (\alpha e^2/R) \tag{3.23}$$

in which

$$B_n = \sum_j p_{ij}^{-n} \quad \text{and} \quad \alpha = \sum_j (\pm)p_{ij}^{-1}$$

The term α is known as the "Madelung constant," and may be calculated precisely for different crystal structures. Methods of evaluation have been discussed elsewhere (e.g., by Kittel, 1957), and the results of such calculations for a variety of crystal structures have been summarized by Sherman (1932); typical results are summarized in Table 3. The form of the variation

Table 3. Typical Values of the Madelung Constant α Corresponding to Different Crystal Structures, Calculated by Sherman (1932)

Structure	α
Sodium chloride	1.747558
Cesium chloride	1.762670
Zinc blende	1.6381
Wurtzite	1.641

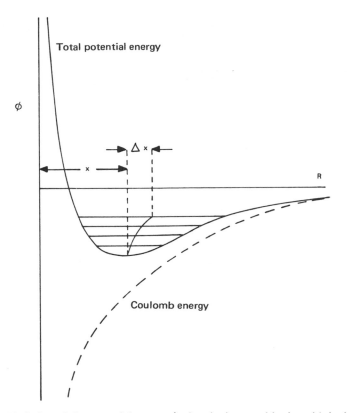

Fig. 15.   Variation of the potential energy ϕ of an ionic crystal lattice with ionic separation R.

of ϕ with interionic separation is illustrated in Fig. 15, from which it is clear that the separation x, corresponding to the minimum in the potential energy curve, is the equilibrium separation. At this equilibrium separation $\partial\phi/\partial R = 0$. Applying this condition to Eq. (3.23) and hence eliminating AB_n produces the result

$$\phi = (\alpha e^2/x)[1 - (1/n)] \qquad (3.24)$$

The total lattice energy Φ of an assembly of N ions will be $(N/2)\phi$. Applying this result to Eq. (3.24) gives

$$\Phi = -(N\alpha e^2/2x)[1 - (1/n)] \qquad (3.25)$$

Elastic constant measurements may be applied to these results to estimate the lattice energy of a crystal at $T = 0$ in the following way.

Writing the first law of thermodynamics as $d\Phi = -P\,dV$ under these circumstances, the bulk modulus K becomes

$$K = -V(dp/dV) = V(d^2\Phi/dV^2)_{T=0}$$

Substituting for the total number of molecules, changing the variable from V to R, and developing the result leads to the equation

$$K = (n-1)e^2\alpha/18x^4 \qquad (3.26)$$

in the case of the rocksalt structure. From a knowledge of K obtained from extrapolation of c_{11} and c_{12} to $T = 0$, Eq. (3.26) may be used to estimate the exponent n of the repulsive force law. Similarly, by eliminating n between Eqs. (3.25) and (3.26), the lattice energy Φ at $T = 0$ may be calculated. Results of such calculations are in good agreement with values based upon experimental thermochemical data, examples of which are provided in the works of Marshall and Miller (1967) on KF and Vallin et al. (1964) on CsBr and CsI.

   Another class of ionic solids in which there is a good deal of interest is that consisting of halides of thallium. Under the influence of a pressure of 5.5 kbar RbCl undergoes a phase transition from the face-centered structure to the body-centered structure, accompanied by a 14% change of volume and an abrupt change in physical properties (see, e.g., Bridgman, 1928; Voronov and Goncharova, 1966; Voronov et al., 1967). Systems such as these automatically adjust themselves to the phase having the lowest Gibbs free energy. A phase transition of this type occurs in TlI also, the structure of which changes from double-layered orthorhombic to the body-centered cubic structure at approximately 170°C under a pressure of 1 bar, or under a pressure of approximately 4.7 kbar at 25°C. The chloride and bromide of thallium have also aroused interest, partly because of their body-centered cubic structure, and attention may be drawn to the elastic constant measurements of Morse and Lawson (1967) and Vallin et al. (1966). Nikanorov et al. (1965) and Nikanorov and Stepanov (1965) have drawn attention to the existence of an increase in the magnitude of the anisotropy factor $A = 2c_{44}/(c_{11} - c_{12})$ accompanying a rise in temperature in the face-centered cubic alkali halides. On the other hand, the anisotropy factors of CsBr and TlBr have negative temperature coefficients. Examination of the experimental results reveals that these differences in behavior arise from the relatively rapid temperature variation of the shear modulus along the [110] axis having polarization in the [110] direction in the face-centered cubic alkali halides, i.e., $(c_{11} - c_{12})/2$, and the relatively rapid temperature variation of the shear modulus along the [100] axis, i.e., c_{44}, in the body-centered cubic ionic solids. There can be little doubt that these similarities between characteristics of the elastic constants of CsBr and TlBr, and the differences between their behavior and that of the alkali halides with the rocksalt structure, arise from the similarity of crystal structure of CsBr and TlBr.

The alkaline earth fluorides form another interesting class of ionic compounds, possessing overall cubic symmetry. The structure of these solids may be regarded as resulting from the interpenetration of three face-centered cubic lattices, one of alkaline earth ions and two of fluorine ions, such that each alkaline earth ion is surrounded by eight fluorine ions, each fluorine ion is surrounded by four alkaline earth ions, and all ions are equally separated. The elastic constants of CaF_2 have been measured in the temperature range 4–300°K by Huffman and Norwood (1960) and those of SrF_2 and BaF_2 have been measured in the same range by Gerlich (1964a,b). The elastic constants extrapolated to 0°K all diminish with increase of mass of the alkaline earth ion, and although the differences between the

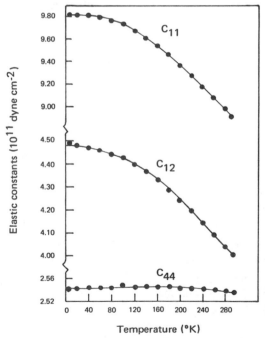

Fig. 16.   The elastic constants of barium fluoride as a function of temperature (after Gerlich, 1964a).

300 and 4.2°K values of c_{11} and c_{12} increase in magnitude with the mass of the alkaline earth ion from approximately 6% to 10% from CaF_2 to BaF_2, the corresponding percentage change in c_{44} with temperature is a reduction from approximately 6% in the case of CaF_2 to practically zero in the case of BaF_2, as shown in Fig. 16. On the basis of Born's theory of crystal lattices, Srinivasan (1958) assumed the validity of a rigid ion model in which he supposed the existence of a repulsive force between ions proportional to x^{-10}. The fluorine structure was of particular interest because Born's theory actually predicted a finite value of $(c_{12} - c_{44})$, i.e., a finite anisotropy was expected from the fact that the fluorine atoms did not occupy positions of centers of symmetry. Agreement between values of the elastic constants of CaF_2 calculated assuming the frequency of the principal Raman line is reasonably good. The calculated anisotropy factor itself is less precise, however, since this involves the difference of two calculated quantities.

3.5. THE PRESSURE DEPENDENCE OF THE ELASTIC CONSTANTS

We saw earlier that the Grüneisen parameter provides a measure of the volume dependence of the frequencies of lattice vibrations. It is possible to describe this variation in a continuum model by the addition of terms of the third order in the strain components to the elastic strain energy. In a valuable review article on the subject Thurston (1967) has described the calculation of the first and second pressure derivatives of the lattice parameters from the second-order elastic constants and their pressure derivatives in detail, which is beyond the scope of the present summary. He has also given extrapolation formulas from which the lattice parameters may be determined at very high pressures. The formulas have been tested successfully with the aid of direct X-ray determinations of the lattice parameters of quartz, magnesium, and cadmium at very high pressures.

Useful tests of the consequences of theoretical models concerned with the vibrations of atoms in solids may be made using experimental data on the pressure dependences of the volume compressibilities of simple solids, such as were furnished by Perez–Albuerne and Drickamer (1965) for crystals conforming to the NaCl and CsCl structures. Fuller information may be derived from measurements of elastic constants in individual directions within a lattice, however.

Using the pulse method mentioned earlier, Lazarus (1949) measured the adiabatic velocities of sound for longitudinal and transverse waves in single-crystal specimens of KCl, NaCl, CuZn, Cu, and Al as functions of pressure up to pressures of the order of 10 kbar. He found that the anisotropy increased in crystals which were not close-packed, but decreased in closest-packed structures. Using these data and also those obtained by Daniels and Smith (1958), Sheard (1958) applied an anisotropic continuum model to calculate the Grüneisen parameters of several solids at low and high temperatures. The high-temperature limiting values calculated for the dielectric solids KCl and NaCl were in very good agreement with values based upon measurements of specific heat, thermal expansion, and elastic constants. The measurement of thermal expansion at temperatures in the vicinity of $T = 0$ poses particularly difficult problems, however, in consequence of which comparisons of low-temperature values of γ derived by the two techniques are seldom possible. In cases where reliable comparisons have been possible, however, agreement has been extremely good, and it is now generally accepted that one of the most convenient means of determining the low-temperature limiting value of the Grüneisen parameter of a solid is from a knowledge of the pressure variation of its elastic constants. Because of experimental difficulties, results of such measurements at low temperatures are seldom available, but it is generally agreed that any influence from the variation with temperature of the pressure variation of the elastic constants is likely to be very small. Experimental support for this contention was provided by the work of Bartels and Schuele (1965), who measured the pressure derivatives of the elastic constants of NaCl and KCl at 195 and 295°K. We saw earlier that in relating the individual parameters γ_j, which describe the volume dependences of the individual frequencies ν_j in a vibrational frequency distribution, to the Grüneisen parameter $\gamma = \beta V / C_V \chi_T$, the weight for each normal mode is taken as its contribution to C_V. Within the limitations of the quasiharmonic approximation any temperature dependence of γ arises through the temperature dependence of the weighting factors, the γ_j themselves being supposed to be temperature-independent. In principle, a knowledge of the effect of temperature on the pressure derivatives of the elastic constants gives information concerning the possible dependence upon temperature and volume of the γ_j values. Although one or two trends were observed, the precision of the experimental data was not sufficiently high to permit firm conclusions in this search for an explicit temperature dependence of γ_j. Perhaps the most important outcome from the work was provided by the result of comparisons of the low-temperature limiting values of γ_0, which were derived from extrapolations of the values derived from the high-pressure measurements at 195 and 295°K. These values were compared with values which by this time had been made available by the very-low-temperature thermal expansion measurements of

White (1961c). The agreement was excellent, thereby drawing attention to the value of high-pressure measurements of this type.

Z. P. Chang *et al.* (1967) measured the single-crystal elastic constants of CsCl up to 4 kbar pressure and of CsBr and CsI up to 10 kbar pressure. The solids were observed to remain stable up to these pressures. On the basis of the positive pressure dependence of the elastic constants, they concluded that there was no evidence for a high-pressure phase transition in these salts. Following a report of a negative temperature dependence of the dielectric constants of thallous halides at high frequencies and a positive temperature dependence at low frequencies, Morse and Lawson (1967) undertook measurements of the temperature and pressure dependences of the elastic constants of TlBr, as mentioned in Section 3.4. Their investigations led them to conclude that the pressure coefficients of the elastic moduli were all positive, while the temperature coefficients were all negative, in common with other ionic crystals. However, they also found that while the anisotropy $[2c_{44}/(c_{11} - c_{12})]$ for the NaCl-type compounds had a positive temperature coefficient, the converse was true of TlBr. The authors concluded that the negative temperature dependence of the dielectric constant could not be attributed to the isothermal compressibility. Measurement on the pressure derivatives of elastic constants have been extended to CaF_2 by Ho and Ruoff (1967) and Wong and Schuele (1967). The latter workers derived values of the Grüneisen parameter from their measurements in the low- and high-temperature limits. The first of these values agreed well with a result based upon low-temperature thermal expansion measurements by White, though the latter value was substantially lower than the result corresponding to thermal expansion measurements. This latter observation was taken to indicate that the average γ_j values of the high-frequency modes are greater than those of the low-frequency modes.

There can be no doubt that extensions of investigations of elastic constants from studies of their temperature dependence to studies of their dependence upon pressure are augmenting experimental lattice-dynamical measurements in a very valuable way. The value of such measurements will be increased further as the temperature range of the investigations is extended, particularly as it is extended to lower temperatures.

Chapter 4

The Thermal Expansion of Solids

4.1. THE PHENOMENON OF THERMAL EXPANSION

Returning to Fig. 15, it will be observed that the curve of potential energy against interatomic separation is not symmetric about the minimum at the equilibrium distance x. In particular, a smaller change of potential energy will accompany a given increase in the separation than will accompany a corresponding decrease. Thus an increase in the energy of longitudinal vibrations, caused by a rise in temperature, will result in an increase of x by an amount such as Δx, as depicted in the figure. This is one way of picturing how the anharmonic nature of the vibrations causes thermal expansion. It turns out that for $T \gg \theta$ there is generally an approximately linear relationship between ϕ and Δx, giving rise to an approximately constant value of the corresponding expansion coefficient. For $T < \theta$, on the other hand, ϕ is not even approximately proportional to T, and the expansion coefficient falls. Barron (1957) has represented the forces on an atom in a matrix by a system of harmonic springs fixed at their extremities, as illustrated in Fig. 17. Since the springs are harmonic, the resultant force on the atom when this is displaced from O to X is independent of the spring length (which corresponds to the lattice spacing). The components of the forces along XA and XC in the direction XO depends upon the tensions in XA and XC, however, and both these tensions and the restoring component caused by them will increase with the spring length (or lattice spacing). The frequency of vibration of X will increase also, giving a situation corresponding to negative expansion. We shall see that this phenomenon manifests itself in semiconductors and in anisotropic solids, both of which display negative expansion under the appropriate conditions. On the other hand, this should

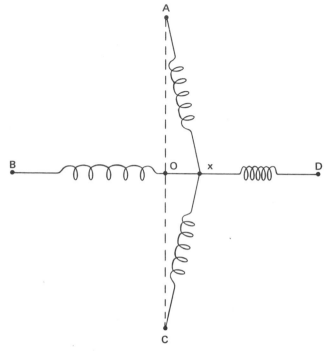

Fig. 17. Model representing the vibration of an atom (●) along the direction *BD* under the influence of springs obeying Hooke's law, fixed at their extremities.

not be confused with negative expansion arising from magnetic interactions exhibited by, e.g., chromium and invar (see White, 1961*b*). Before looking at some of the experimental results which have been obtained for various solids it will be useful to survey the more important experimental methods of measuring thermal expansion.

4.2. EXPERIMENTAL METHODS OF MEASURING THERMAL EXPANSION

Because of the theoretical interest in the variation of linear coefficients of expansion with temperature, particularly at temperatures below ambient, methods have been developed which may be applied to specimens of relatively small size, which may be accommodated conveniently in cryostats. The methods may be classified broadly into those possessing intermediate sensitivities $\Delta l/l$ of the order of 10^{-5}–10^{-6} and those having sensitivities of the order of 10^{-8}–10^{-9}. In this notation Δl is the smallest length change which may be detected in a specimen of length l. The advantage of the latter methods is clearly the increased precision to which they lend themselves, and the potential ability to measure expansion at temperatures close to absolute zero, at which temperature the coefficients of expansion of all solids become zero. The corresponding limitation of the intermediate-sensitivity methods is equally clear, although methods in this class frequently possess advantages over higher-sensitivity methods, e.g., in continuity of operation, in the existence of fewer restrictions on the overall length change which may be measured, in the ability to measure coefficients of expansion in temperature ranges in which these are changing rapidly with temperature, and in the ability to make absolute measurements. Exceptions may be found to most classifications, however, and each method should be considered on its own particular merits.

4.2.1. Optical Methods

Perhaps the most outstanding early method of any notable precision which was suitable for use with small specimens was that due to Fizeau (see, e.g., 1864, 1866). The method involved preparing blocks from crystals and polishing one of the faces. The crystal under investigation was stood on a table, above which was supported a glass plate. A beam of approximately monochromatic light was directed down on to the system, and reflections occurred from the lower surface of the glass plate and the upper face of the specimen. When these two faces were adjusted to be at a small angle to each other the two reflected beams interferred upon being combined, and movements of the fringe pattern accompanying subsequent temperature changes allowed the coefficient of thermal expansion to be measured relative to the expansion of the supports. Repeating the observations with the specimen absent facilitated allowance for the expansion of the supports. This method has been employed by a number of later workers, e.g., by Buffington and Latimer (1926), Merritt (1933), Nix and MacNair (1941), Rubin *et al.* (1954), Waterhouse and Yates (1968).

The main difference between the later versions and that of Fizeau lies in the use of quartz or glass optical flats between adjacent faces of which the interference is arranged to take place when these are separated by the specimen under investigation. This may take the form of three small pieces or a single, hollow, cylindrical specimen. Additional advantages of the later systems lie in improvements in the measurement of absolute values and differences of temperature, and improvements of the precision with which fringe movements may be measured. The division of methods into "high" and "intermediate" sensitivity is somewhat artificial, since improvements are constantly resulting in increases in sensitivity, and there exist variations of detail within methods based upon a common principle of operation which result in variations of sensitivity within any one class. Taking the interferometric method as an example of this point, Rubin *et al.* (1954) produced circular fringes by directing a nonparallel beam of light on to parallel optical flats, producing a system capable of detecting values of $\Delta l/l$ of approximately 3×10^{-7}; Meincke and Graham (1965) used a Fabry–Perot etalon with a sensitivity $\Delta l/l$ of approximately 4×10^{-9} when using specimens 2 in. long. Waterhouse and Yates (1968) have described improvements to earlier versions of a Fizeau system with which a sensitivity of approximately 10^{-7} has been achieved. As a representative example of the interferometric method, this apparatus will be described in some detail.

The apparatus represents an improvement over earlier versions of the Fizeau arrangement employed by Yates and Panter (1962) and James and Yates (1965). The mechanism of specimen accommodation and fringe formation was identical to that of the latter workers, a diagram of whose specimen chamber is shown in Fig. 18. The interferometer consisted of two circular quartz optical flats, separated by a hollow, cylindrical specimen S (o.d. 2.7 cm, i.d. 1.8 cm, and height 1 cm) from which three projecting feet had been filed top and bottom. The two faces of the upper flat (thickness 0.45 cm and diameter 2.7 cm) and the upper surface of the lower flat (thickness 0.45 cm and diameter 3.0 cm) were polished flat to within 1/20th of a nominal wavelength of visible light. The two faces of the upper flat were cut at an angle of $40'$ to each other, so as to throw unwanted reflections out of the field of view, and the visibility of the fringes was improved markedly by partially aluminizing the lower surface of the upper flat and fully aluminizing the upper surface of the lower flat. The lower flat was placed between two brass rings, which were connected by three thin foil strips. This restricted the lateral movement of the flat with respect to the ring assembly, meanwhile allowing for differential contraction, and the lower ring was located in a groove within the copper specimen chamber C. The specimen was contained by the upper ring on the lower flat, on which it stood. Lateral movement of the upper optical flat was controlled by the grooved collar R, fitting loosely on its upper surface.

The stability of the interference pattern was much improved by maintaining the interferometer assembly in slight compression by means of the helical brass spring H. The lower extremity of this spring was soldered to R,

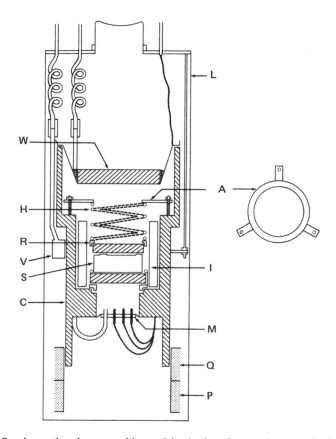

Fig. 18. Specimen chamber assembly used in the interferometric method of measuring thermal expansion at low temperatures (after James and Yates, 1965): L, outer jacket; A, spring compression ring; I, indium resistance thermometer; M, metal–glass seal; Q, copper sensing element; P, heating coil; W, window; H, helical brass spring; R, grooved collar; V, vapor pressure bulb; S, specimen; C, specimen chamber.

while the upper extremity was soldered to the ring A, which was positioned and controlled by three spring-loaded leveling screws. The top of the specimen chamber was sealed by the 0.6-cm-thick, optically flat glass window W, of diameter 4.5 cm, the latter being sealed by Araldite into the 0.008-in-thick truncated cone of spun copper. This mount was attached to the specimen chamber by Wood's metal, and could easily be removed. Details of the indium resistance thermometer have been given by James and Yates (1963). The 40-swg copper wires to this thermometer, which were thermally anchored to the specimen chamber, and also a 2-mm-bore German silver tube to allow for the passage of helium exchange gas, entered the specimen chamber by a metal–glass seal M. The vapor pressure bulb V was used for condensation of nitrogen or hydrogen in periodic checks on the thermometer calibration. The specimen chamber was supported by three adjustable, 2-mm-bore German silver tubes from the top of the brass jacket L, which was immersed in liquid nitrogen or liquid hydrogen. The space between C and L was normally evacuated, and observations were made at temperatures maintained steady to within $0.01°K$ with the aid of the heater P and the copper sensing element Q, which formed part of an automatic temperature controller based upon a design of Parkinson and Quarrington (1954). Details of the means of getting light into and out of the specimen chamber, which formed the subject of a conventional cryostat, may be found in the original paper.

The main difference between this interferometer and its predecessors lay in the fiduciary system and in the fringe movement detection system. Referring to Fig. 19(a), a fully aluminized strip A was deposited on the partially aluminized lower surface of the upper flat. With the interferometer assembled this lay above the region B of the fully aluminized upper surface of the lower flat, on which a piece of black tape had been attached, presenting the appearance of Fig. 19(b), in which Fizeau fringes are shown in the rest of the field of view. Figure 20 shows the appearance of the interferometer in relation to the observation slits. The slits were lined up on the fiduciary and fringe systems as shown, through which light passed to a photomultiplier arrangement, the detector of the system being a galvanometer. Each slit was masked in the appropriate sequence, and the galvanometer was calibrated in terms of fringe displacements resulting from alterations of the pressure of the exchange gas between the interferometer plates by carefully

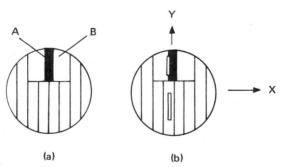

(a)   (b)

Fig. 19. Appearance of the interferometer used by Waterhouse and Yates (1968): (a) Plan view of interferometer showing fully aluminized strip A on lower surface of upper flat over blackened region B of upper surface of lower flat. (b) Plan view showing slits in relation to fiduciary and fringe systems.

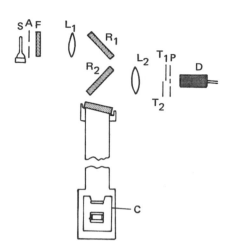

Fig. 20. Optical system employed in the low-temperature thermal expansion work of Waterhouse and Yates (1968): S, mercury lamp; A, aperture; F, filter; L_1, collimating lens; R_1, fully aluminized glass plate; R_2, partially aluminized glass plate; C, specimen chamber; L_2, image focusing lens; T_1, T_2, shutters; P, slits; D, photomultiplier tube detector.

measured amounts. Fringe movements accompanying dimensional changes of specimens resulting from temperature changes could then be measured and used to calculate the linear coefficient of thermal expansion of the specimen. A high-precision sighting was achieved by a procedure which enabled attention to be concentrated on one of the parts of the fringe system in which intensity was changing most rapidly with distance across the pattern.

The system as described has been improved further by replacing the vapor lamp, which formed the original source of illumination, by a laser possessing high-amplitude stability. The additional stability reduces errors which would otherwise arise from time-dependent intensity variations, and the increased intensity produces greater contrast in the interference fringe pattern. An additional improvement is in hand to avoid interruptions in a sequence of measurements which may be caused by intermittent fringe rotations resulting from background mechanical shocks to the system. One of the main advantages of this system over other interferometric methods lies in the fact that observations are always made at the same position of the interferometer, thus making the method a null one and removing limitations imposed by the flatness of the interferometer plates. Pojur and Yates (1968) have drawn attention to a further possible increase in the sensitivity of the interferometric method by the use of moiré fringes formed from Fizeau fringes.

A second type of optical method is the photometer method due to Andres (1961). The essential features of the mechanism are shown in Fig. 21. The system consisted of two grids constructed from optically flat pieces of glass on which chromium had been deposited and upon which lines had

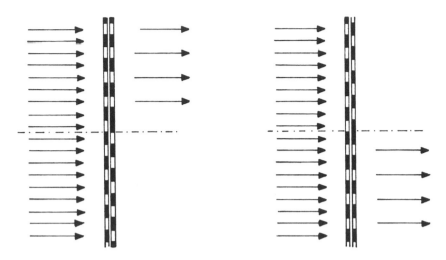

Fig. 21.   Optical grids used by Andres (1961).

been scratched with a discontinuity in the spacing, as shown. The principle of operation was to maintain one grating fixed, while dilatational changes in the specimen were communicated to the second grid. If the disposition of the grids resembled the arrangement shown in Fig. 21(a), it is clear that light might pass freely through the upper half of the assembly, while none would pass through the lower half. The reverse is true in the case shown in Fig. 21(b), while in general a limited amount of light would be passed by both halves, the relative amounts being a periodic function of the relative displacement. The arrangement was housed in a cryostat, light being piped into and out of the grids via Perspex light pipes. The device was calibrated with the aid of a micrometer screw mechanism, and temperature measurement was achieved with a carbon resistance thermometer. The sensitivity $\Delta l/l$ claimed for the system was approximately 10^{-9}.

A third basic type of optical method is provided by the optical lever. A valuable review of the development of this method of detecting and measuring small displacements has been given by Jones (1961). A typical system in this class is shown in Fig. 22, in which an image of the source is focused onto the mirror M by the lens L_1. The lens L_2, which is identical to L_1, transmits this image to the split photocell D. In a subsidiary system an image of the grid G_1 is cast on the grid G_2 with the aid of lens L_3. The spacings of the gratings G_1 and G_2 resemble those of the Andres setup in that when light from the upper half of G_1 can pass through G_2, light passing through the lower half of G_1 will be stopped by G_2. A prism P deflects the light such that the light from half of the system falls on one photocell while

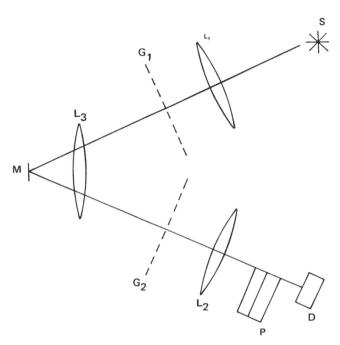

Fig. 22. A typical optical lever system: S, source; L_1, L_2, L_3, lenses; G_1, G_2, grids; M, concave mirror; D, split photocell; P, prism.

the light from the other half falls on the other photocell. A slight rotation of M thus results in the image of G_1 moving over G_2, which in turn results in a change in the difference of the responses of the two photocells.

An alternative form of optical lever was used in low-temperature thermal expansion measurements by Huzan et $al.$ (1961) in their work on aluminum, in which a sensitivity $\Delta l/l$ of 6×10^{-8} was claimed, but an adaptation of a system closely resembling that of Jones was applied by Shapiro et $al.$ (1964) to measure the thermal expansion of copper at low temperatures. The expansion of the specimen, which took the form of a rod of length 8 cm, was communicated to a doubly twisted "Ayrton" strip constructed of copper $+$ 1.9% beryllium, the cross section of which was 0.55 mm by 0.035 mm. A small mirror, corresponding to M of Fig. 22, was attached to the center of the strip, and in this way a system was developed for which the authors claimed a sensitivity $\Delta l/l$ of 4×10^{-11}. A later variation of the optical lever has been described by Bunton and Weintroub (1968), in which a combined adaptation of a lever-grid assembly has been employed to achieve a sensitivity $\Delta l/l$ of approximately 2×10^{-9}.

4.2.2. X-Ray Methods

If the lattice parameter of a crystal is measured at two different temperatures, its thermal expansion may clearly be calculated. One advantage which the X-ray method shares with the interferometric method over some methods lies in the absolute nature of the thermal expansion coefficients to which it leads. A second advantage lies in the fact that it gives a measure of expansion uncomplicated by dimensional changes resulting from vacancy formation, from the presence of impurities, or from any other cause. Offsetting these advantages to some extent is the fact that the sensitivity is not generally as high as those of some of the other methods. Figgins *et al.* (1956) described an application of this method to a polycrystalline specimen of aluminum. The X-ray system resembled a modified powder camera, at the center of which the specimen was mounted against a hollow copper block. The temperature of the block could be controlled by the combined effects of precooled hydrogen gas flowing through it and heat produced in a heater wound on the block. With this system measurements were conducted over the approximate temperature range 20–300°K, in which a sensitivity $\Delta l/l$ of approximately 5×10^{-6} was claimed. In a later application of the X-ray method Batchelder and Simmons (1965) constructed the camera, including the source of X-rays, on a large goniometer. The specimen crystal was meanwhile located within an independent cryostat or furnace of up to 25 cm diameter. The authors claimed a sensitivity $\Delta l/l$ of approximately 3×10^{-6} with their oscillating camera, with which they performed some excellent work on a variety of solids.

4.2.3. Electrical Methods

An electrical device which has been used for measuring small displacements for many years is the capacitor. A small movement of one of the plates of a capacitor results in a change in capacity which may be measured electronically, and this change may be related to the corresponding linear displacement. One of the earlier applications of this technique to the measurement of thermal expansion at low temperatures was that due to Bijl and Pullan (1955), who incorporated the capacitor in the tank circuit of a radiofrequency Colpitts oscillator. With this arrangement the authors claimed a sensitivity $\Delta l/l$ of approximately 6×10^{-7}.

A more recent adaptation of the capacitor dilatometer to work of this nature is that due to White (1961*a*); a later model of this instrument is due to Carr *et al.* (1964), and later workers have constructed systems which are essentially similar. White's apparatus, as used by Carr *et al.* (1964), is shown

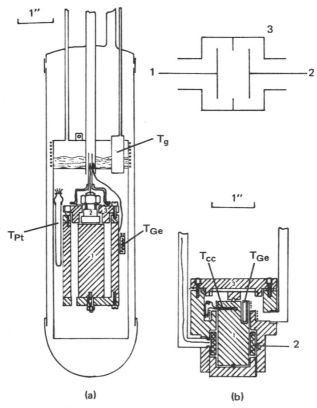

Fig. 23. The capacitive dilatometer of Carr *et al.* (1964). Electrical capacitance between 1 and 2 is measured. Parts marked 3 form a guard-ring and grounding shield. (a) Differential cell, (b) absolute cell.

in Fig. 23, in the upper right-hand corner of which the principle of the system is depicted. The capacitances of the three-terminal capacitor are compared to parts in 10^8 with the aid of a bridge circuit based upon that of Thompson (1958). Relating this diagram to that of the cryostat, the specimen itself is represented by 1, and its upper face is polished flat, forming one electrode. The components labeled 2 and 3 in the cryostat diagram correspond to those bearing the same numbers in the capacitor diagram, the capacitance between 1 and 2 being measured, while 3 forms the guard ring and grounding shield. The system is essentially a comparative one, giving the expansion of the specimen relative to that of the containing chamber. The absolute cell, shown in the lower right-hand corner, was used to give an absolute measurement of the linear coefficient of thermal expansion of the material of the differential cell, i.e., copper. Temperatures above 11°K were measured with the aid of a platinum resistance thermometer T_{Pt}. Between 4.2 and 11°K a germanium thermometer T_{Ge} was used to supplement a helium gas thermometer T_g, providing a sensitivity measure of the steadiness of the cell temperature. A similar thermometer T_{Ge} was included in the absolute cell, this one being used below 40°K, and at higher temperatures the copper–constantan thermocouple T_{cc} was used to measure temperatures between the specimen and the cell wall, which is maintained at one of a number of possible known constant temperatures.

Full details of the capacitance bridge are given in the original article, but a design showing the construction of one of the reference capacitors is shown in Fig. 24. These are packed in expanded polystyrene boxes and housed in a temperature-controlled room so that their values do not generally drift by more than a few parts in 10^8 per hour. The apparatus possesses a sensitivity $\Delta l/l$ of approximately 2×10^{-10}, and it was the forerunner of the high-sensitivity methods which have opened up a whole new field of work in thermal expansion at helium temperatures. The apparatus has now been used by White and co-workers in investigating the thermal expansions of a wide variety of solids at these temperatures, and the results of their efforts represent one of the major experimental contributions to low-temperature lattice dynamics in recent years.

Another successful electrical method having a high sensitivity is the variable transformer system described by Carr and Swenson (1964), which

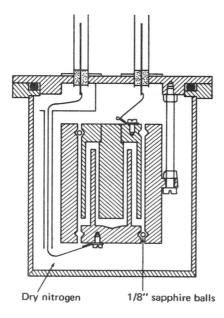

Fig. 24.   Diagram of a stable 10 pF three-terminal capacitance of the type used by Carr *et al.* (1964). The Invar capacitor was supported in a brass box filled with dry nitrogen.

Dry nitrogen   1/8″ sapphire balls

has been used in exploring the expansion coefficients of a number of substances. Essentially, the windings on the secondary coil of a transformer are wound in opposite directions. When this coil is centered within the primary coil there is no net flux linkage between the two coils. Upon moving the secondary with respect to the primary, the mutual inductance changes, and this change may be used as a measure of the linear displacement causing it. Thermal expansion of the specimen is communicated to the secondary coil, thermal isolation of the specimen being achieved with the aid of sapphire spacers at each end. The mutual inductance bridge, details of which may be found in the original paper, was capable of detecting changes in mutual inductance of as little as 10^{-9} %, and the sensitivity $\Delta l/l$ claimed for the overall system was approximately 3×10^{-10}.

The experimental determination of the linear coefficient of expansion of a solid involves two types of measurement, one of which is the measurement of small length changes. It has been seen that a variety of ingenious ideas have been devised for this purpose, but these must not be allowed to overshadow the importance of precise temperature control and measurement. It is essential that the relationship between the temperature recorded by the thermometer used in one of these systems and the temperature of the specimen should be known exactly. Ideally, one would like the two to be identical, but it is not always possible to achieve this precisely. Furthermore, it is generally preferable to conduct measurements at steady temperatures, for in dynamic methods any difference of temperature between the specimen and thermometer requires particularly careful control. Various temperature controllers have been described in the literature (e.g., Parkinson and Quarrington, 1954; Dauphinee and Woods, 1955; Rose-Innes, 1964), but a recent one which may be given special mention is that of Gluyas et al. (1970), with which a temperature stability of $0.01°K$ or better can be achieved.

4.3. SOME EXPERIMENTAL RESULTS

4.3.1. Alkali Halides with the Rocksalt Structure

Measurements have been undertaken on a wide variety of alkali halides with the rocksalt structure, e.g., on LiF, NaF, NaCl, NaI, KCl, KBr, KI, RbBr, and RbI. The measurements have been extended down to low temperatures, and in some cases up to high temperatures (e.g., Leadbetter and Newsham, 1969). With the exception of LiF, in which the atoms are packed particularly closely, the Grüneisen parameters of these solids fall from a high-temperature limiting value γ_∞ to a low-temperature limiting value γ_0. Furthermore, there is a greater systematic increase in $(\gamma_\infty - \gamma_0)$ as the mass of the alkali ion is increased for a given halide ion than is observed when the mass of the halide ion is increased for a given alkali ion, e.g.,

$$\begin{array}{cccc}
 & \text{NaI} \rightarrow & \text{KI} \rightarrow & \text{RbI} \\
(\gamma_\infty - \gamma_0) & 0.67 & 1.19 & >1.60
\end{array}$$

$$\begin{array}{cccc}
 & \text{NaF} \rightarrow & \text{NaCl} \rightarrow & \text{NaI} \\
(\gamma_\infty - \gamma_0) & 0.43 & 0.64 & 0.67
\end{array}$$

This observation has been interpreted as an indication of the predominance of the alkali ion over the halide ion in determining interionic forces.

4.3.2. Alkali Halides with the Cesium Chloride Structure

The results contained in Table 4 are taken from Bailey and Yates (1967a) and Kirkham and Yates (1968), from which it will be seen that (a)

Table 4. Grüneisen Parameters γ of CsCl, CsBr, and CsI as Functions of Temperature (after Bailey and Yates, 1967a; Kirkham and Yates, 1968)

T, °K	γ		
	CsCl	CsBr	CsI
0	—	(1.9)	—
25	1.98	2.01	2.01
30	2.03	2.08	2.01
40	2.06	2.13	2.01
50	2.09	2.13	2.01
60	2.11	2.10	2.01
80	2.10	2.09	2.00
100	2.08	2.08	2.01
120	2.09	2.08	2.02
140	2.10	2.07	2.01
160	2.10	2.07	2.01
180	2.10	2.06	2.01
200	2.10	2.06	2.00
220	2.09	2.06	2.01
240	2.08	2.06	2.01
260	2.07	2.05	2.01
270	2.06	2.05	2.01

γ is sensibly independent of temperature, and (b) increasing the mass of the halide ion has no apparent effect on γ. These observations are both in accordance with predictions of Ganesan and Srinivasan (1963), who incorporated the Coulomb potential between the ions and a nearest-neighbor interaction varying as r^{-n}. An examination of available elastic data led to the conclusion that $n \approx 15$, which was at the limit of the range $15 \leq n \leq 20$ over which $\gamma_0 - \gamma_\infty$ was expected to change sign. The authors also concluded that varying the ratio of ionic masses would have only a slight effect on γ.

4.3.3. Molecular Solids

In the case of crystals in which the molecules are well-defined units, it is sometimes possible to analyze thermodynamic data so as to give information about translational and librational vibrations of the molecules and about vibrations of the atoms within the molecules, provided that the spectra do not overlap. Leadbetter (1965) has performed a very successful analysis along these lines for ice.

4.3.4. Semiconductors

Some years ago both Barron (1957) and Blackman (1958) concluded that negative thermal expansion was possible if the contribution to γ from the transverse modes of vibration outweighed the longitudinal contribution. It was also concluded that negative expansion coefficients were to be expected from open structures rather than close-packed ones, and that those with relatively low shear moduli would be favored. Elemental and compound semiconductors satisfy these requirements, and in all the cases examined negative expansion is observed over a range of low temperature, e.g., in Si, Ge, ZnS, ZnSe, GaAs, GaSb, CdSe, CdTe, InSb, HgSe.

4.3.5. Glasses

It was mentioned in Section 2.4.1 that those lower-frequency modes of vibration in glass that are affected by neutron irradiation also appear to be influenced by network-filling additives. In fact, White (1964a) found that when glass was doped with concentrations amounting to a few per cent of alumina or borate, no noticeable effect was produced in the thermal expansion. On the other hand, when comparable percentages of monovalent or divalent additives such as sodium, potassium, or calcium were introduced

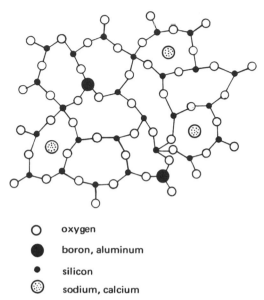

○	oxygen
●	boron, aluminum
•	silicon
⊛	sodium, calcium

Fig. 25. Two-dimensional representation of a glass network (after Stevels, 1962).

very marked changes were observed. It was known that the first of these impurities entered the lattice substitutionally, whereas the last-named impurities entered the spaces in the network (see Fig. 25). This led to the conclusion that the vibrations in question were most likely to be caused by transverse vibrations of the oxygen atoms. This provides a very direct example of an instance in which more information about the vibrations of the atoms in a solid may be derived from measurements of specific heat and thermal expansion taken together than is given by either separately.

4.3.6. Polymers

One of the more extensive pieces of experimental thermal expansion work conducted on polymers must be that due to Laquer and Head (1952), in which specimens of reinforced, condensation, and vinyl polymers from both rods and sheets were examined between 20 and 320°K. The thermal expansion coefficients are generally quite high at room temperature, and points of inflection were observed in the temperature variations in some instances, explanations of which are not immediately obvious. Measurements have been made on methylmethacrylate between 20 and 300°K by Giauque et al. (1952), and Kirby (1956) has worked on polytetrafluoroethylene between 83 and 573°K. Barker (1967) developed a phenomenological "bundle-of-tubes" model to take account of interaction between long-chain polymer molecules, which appeared to be consistent with available experimental data. Systematic investigations of elastic constants for these solids would be particularly valuable in providing the last link in the chain of measurements required to make unambiguous calculations concerning the volume dependence of the vibrational frequencies.

4.3.7. Metals and Magnetic Materials

White (1961b) has reported the presence of an electronic contribution to thermal expansion as exists in specific heats, i.e., when $T \ll \theta$

$$\alpha = AT + BT^3$$

in which the term in T represents the electronic contribution and the term in T^3 is the lattice contribution. A is related in a complex way to the density of states at the Fermi surface. From the electronic contributions to the thermal expansion and specific heat an "electronic Grüneisen parameter" may be defined by

$$\beta_e = \gamma_e C_e \chi_T / V$$

where

$$\gamma_e = 1 + \{\partial [\ln F(\varepsilon_0)]/\partial (\ln V)\}_T$$

$F(\varepsilon_0)$ being the density of states at the Fermi surface and the subscript e being used to denote the electronic contributions. As the volume of a crystal changes, it influences the position of the Fermi energy ε_0 due to dimensional changes of the unit cell, and it changes the shape of the energy surfaces if the coupling between the conduction electrons and the lattice varies.

In magnetic metals entropy S_m may be contributed by magnetic interaction, giving rise to an additional thermal expansion term β_m. Expressing S_m as a function $f(\varepsilon_m/T)$, where ε_m is an interaction energy, β_m may be related to the magnetic contribution to the specific heat C_m by a "magnetic Grüneisen parameter" γ_m, and

$$\beta_m = \gamma_m C_m \chi_T / V$$

where

$$\gamma_m = -[\partial (\ln \varepsilon_m)/\partial (\ln V)]_T$$

Hirschkoff and Wolcott (1965) have drawn attention to the possibility of a further contribution to the thermal expansion of magnetic metals arising from nuclear interaction with the static hyperfine field. According to White, the magnetic contribution to thermal expansion is proportional to T at low temperatures, as is the case for electrons, and for this reason it is not possible to separate the two contributions directly.

According to Lord (1967), a contribution arising from spin waves in ferromagnetics is to be expected in the form $\alpha \propto T^{3/2}$. Guseinov and Seidov (1966) arrived at the same conclusion for ferromagnetics, and in the case of antiferromagnetics they predicted $\alpha = (A/T^2)e^{-B/T}$ at very low temperatures and $\alpha = A + BT + CT^3$ at intermediate temperatures. These predictions await confirmation. The application of a high-sensitivity method of measurement at intermediate temperatures might help to test some of these predictions.

4.3.8. Mixtures and Alloys

Among attempts to understand the thermal expansion of mixtures may be mentioned the model due to Turner (1946), in which it is assumed that it is sufficiently realistic to regard each component as being surrounded by a homogeneous mixture, that the sum of the internal forces may be equated to zero, and that shear deformation may be neglected completely. Pursuing this line of argument, Turner finally arrived at an expression for the thermal expansion of the mixture in terms of the volume coefficients of thermal expansion and bulk moduli of the constituents. Kerner (1956) assumed the existence of an average shell of suspending medium surrounding a grain of an average component of the mixture, sufficiently far beyond which was the average medium, consisting of suspending medium and grains. When considering the equilibrium of the system the ratio of the linear dimensions of an inclusion to those of the whole body was assumed to be equal to the ratio of the corresponding surface areas and volumes, and the case of tightly packed grains was considered by allowing the suspending medium to vanish. Hughes and Brittain (1964) restricted themselves to the case of a dilute solid solution binary alloy, regarding the solute atoms as defects embedded in an elastic continuum. Full details of all three theories may be found in the original works, though all three are inadequate.

Bailey *et al.* (1969) drew attention to the fact that comparisons of experimental observations with these theories had frequently been restricted to systems in which the coefficients of expansion of the components were very similar to one another. For this reason Bailey *et al.* concentrated their attention on alloys of palladium and silver, the expansions of which are quite different. Their measurements drew attention to the inadequacy of these theories, and established the case for the development of a theory of the thermal expansion of mixtures and alloys on an atomic scale.

4.3.9. Anisotropic Solids

In solids which do not possess cubic symmetry it is to be expected that the vibrational frequency spectra of the constituent atoms will be particularly complex. In these cases the directional dependence of the potential energy curve, shown in Fig. 15, will result in the preferential excitation of vibrations in the direction of greatest compressibility at low temperatures, because of the lower frequencies in this direction. This will result in expansion in this crystalline direction which exceeds that in the perpendicular plane. Also, an expansion in this "easy" direction will give rise to a contraction in the perpendicular plane, the effect of which may be to predominate over the small contribution to the expansion, resulting in a net contraction. A number of examples of anisotropic expansion have been studied quantitatively in solids possessing structures which are basically tetragonal, rhombohedral, and hexagonal, e.g., Tl, Y, Be, and Zn (Meyerhoff and Smith, 1962), Bi and Sn (White 1964b, 1969), Mg, Zn, and Cd (McCammon and White, 1965), Zn (Channing and Weintroub, 1965), Sb and Bi (Bunton and Weintroub, 1969), and In (Collins et al., 1967). The effects become particularly pronounced as the forces in the two directions at right angles become increasingly different, e.g., in pyrolytic graphite (Bailey and Yates, 1969). Applications of data of this type, together with the available specific heat and elastic constant data, yield quantitative information concerning the volume variations of the moments of the frequency distribution in a solid. This, in turn, leads to an understanding of the relative magnitude of the interatomic forces in different axial directions (e.g., Barron and Munn, 1967; Bailey and Yates, 1969).

4.3.10. Anomalies

Transformations to the antiferromagnetic state in solids such as MnF_2, $FeCl_2$, etc. are accompanied by λ-type anomalies in the heat capacity at the Néel temperature. Measurements of the specific heat in the neighborhood of the transition give information about the entropy changes involved, and in comparing the results of such measurements with theories of critical behavior it is important to take effects due to exchange striction into account. The theories generally assume fixed lattice dimensions, and hence constant

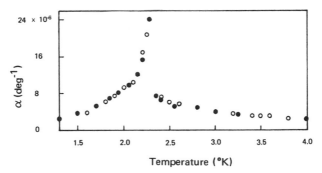

Fig. 26. Plot of experimental results for the linear thermal expansion coefficient α of $CoCl_2 \cdot 6H_2O$ along the b axis (after Donaldson and Lanchester, 1968).

exchange interactions, and the correction of experimental data to take account of dimensional changes is very important. Figure 26 shows an example of the anomaly in thermal expansion which accompanies a transformation from the paramagnetic to the antiferromagnetic state in $CoCl_2 \cdot 6H_2O$.

In considering the similarities of face-centered cubic Invar alloys Fe–Ni (25–50% Ni) and $ZrZn_2$, both of which he regarded as weak itinerant ferromagnets, Wohlfarth (1969) deduced that the discontinuity in the volume thermal expansion coefficient of $ZrZn_2$ should be given by

$$\Delta\beta = -2CM^2(0, 0)/KT_c = -4.0 \times 10^{-6} \quad °K^{-1}$$

at the Curie temperature T_c, in which K is the bulk modulus of elasticity, C is a coupling constant, and $M(H, T)$ the magnetization. The coefficients of $-T$ observed by White (1965) in the negative linear contributions to the volume thermal expansion of two Invar alloys proved to be closely similar to the value predicted for $ZrZn_2$ by Wohlfarth, and this has been taken as evidence for the similarity of the two systems.

4.3.11. Superconductors

White (1962a) has measured the thermal expansion of lead between 1.3 and 12°K. He found that the linear coefficient of expansion was proportional to T^3 when the specimen was in the superconducting state, and that the value in the superconducting state was less than the value in the normal state. From length changes occurring during the isothermal destruction of superconductivity the pressure dependence of the critical field has been calculated.

Extending his observations to the hard superconductors vanadium, niobium, and tantalum, White (1962*b*) observed a lack of reproducibility in length changes at the *s–n* transition. This, together with hysteresis effects, made it impossible to draw unambiguous conclusions about length changes associated with the creation and destruction of the field at fixed temperatures, but these have since been estimated from extrapolations of the thermal expansion versus temperature curves above and below the transition temperatures. The values so obtained have been used to estimate the isothermal pressure dependence of the critical field at the transition temperature, and these results have been used to calculate the fractional variation in the bulk modulus at the transition.

Chapter 5

The Analysis of Thermodynamic Data

5.1. INTRODUCTION

If the displacements of the atoms from their equilibrium positions are small, we may assume that the electrons follow the motions of the nuclei adiabatically, and the potential energy ϕ of the crystalline lattice may be written as a series expansion

$$\phi = \phi_0 + \phi_2 + \phi_3 + \phi_4 + \cdots \tag{5.1}$$

in which the ϕ_n represent all terms containing nth-order displacements, ϕ_0 is the static lattice energy, and ϕ_1 is absent in order to satisfy the condition necessary for equilibrium. If we ignore all terms beyond ϕ_2, this gives the harmonic approximation and leads to Hooke's law forces between atoms and purely harmonic vibrations, as treated by Einstein and Debye. This is completely inadequate to account for properties such as thermal expansion, dependence of the elastic constants upon temperature and pressure, etc. Our earlier remarks have been largely concerned with the specific heat, thermal expansion, and elastic properties of solids considered in semiisolation. The information which can be gained in this way is very limited and much more progress can be made by combining the data and expressing these in terms which may be related to atomic models. It is also important to appreciate the limitations to this kind of analysis. In particular, Barron and Morrison (1960) and Chambers (1961) have shown that detailed information about the frequency spectra cannot, in general, be obtained from inversion of the heat capacities because the vibrational thermodynamic properties depend upon averages over the whole spectrum. However, we can get specific values of these averages, known as the moments of the distribution, which will be defined shortly. Individual moments are particularly important in governing the variation of certain physical properties in particular temperature ranges.

It will be remembered that earlier we had observed deviations from temperature independence in the Debye characteristic temperature, and that Blackman had accounted for the fall in θ which accompanied a rise in temperature from $T = 0$ in terms of a more rapid rise with frequency in the distribution function than is required in the Debye theory. At sufficiently high temperatures, on the other hand, the thermal energy will be sufficiently high to excite all the oscillations contributing to the spectrum. In this case further increase of temperature would not result in further changes of form of the energy content, the specific heat would be expected to level off, and the percentage changes in θ corresponding to a given rise of temperature would diminish. A detailed knowledge of the temperature dependence of θ provides a convenient means of exploring the vibrational behavior of the atoms in some detail, as will become apparent when we apply the quasi-harmonic approximation to the problem.

5.2. THE NATURE OF THE PROBLEM

We have outlined reasons for understanding the departure of graphs of θ versus T from temperature independence at low temperatures, and reasons for expecting to find such independence at high temperatures. In practice, however, departures are found at these temperatures, too, as will be seen from Fig. 27, which shows results for alkali halides with the two structures characteristic of these compounds. In the absence of any ordering processes, deviations from temperature independence of this type are generally attributed to anharmonic effects. In studying vibrations of atoms through thermodynamic data it is customary to attempt to relate properties of models to properties of the solid as they would be expected to be in the absence of anharmonic effects. Once a well-tried, self-consistent scheme has been established, attempts may then be made to use this to study anharmonicity in isolation.

5.3. GENERAL TEMPERATURE CONSIDERATIONS

If we raise the temperature of a body from absolute zero we may, in general, expect to observe two things: (a) that the dimensions of the body should change, and (b) that the dimensions should increase with rise of

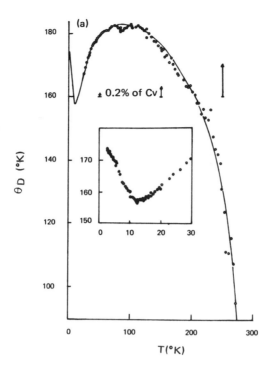

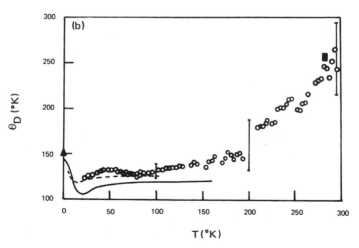

Fig. 27. Debye characteristic temperatures for the two structures of alkali halides as functions of temperature: (a) potassium bromide (after Berg and Morrison, 1957), and (b) cesium bromide. The open circles depict the experimental points and the vertical lines correspond to $\pm$ 1% of C_V (after Kirkham and Yates, 1968).

temperature. There are exceptions to both of these generalizations, but these occurrences would conform with our general experience on the macroscopic scale. On the microscopic scale we should expect the energy content of the vibrations to increase with temperature, giving rise to increased amplitudes of vibration, and we should also be prepared for the nature of the vibrations to change with temperature. Provided that the temperature is not too high, we may take account of the first signs of anharmonicity by allowing the crystal to expand, by supposing that the frequencies of vibration are dependent upon volume, but that they remain harmonic in character. These assumptions form the basis of the quasiharmonic approximation, and these are the terms of reference within which we shall work in establishing a scheme which allows us to calculate the moments of the frequency distributions of simple solids, and their volume dependence. The explicit temperature dependence of the frequencies of vibration at constant volume forms a contribution to the anharmonicity of the vibrations which becomes important at high temperatures. Experience based upon applications of this approach have produced results which are self-consistent, confirming that it is only at temperatures which are much higher than the Debye temperature that explicitly temperature-dependent anharmonic effects are sufficiently marked to permit quantitative experimental investigation using techniques generally available at the present time.

5.4. THE GRÜNEISEN PARAMETER

An alternative and more revealing approach to an understanding of the Grüneisen parameter may be made by thinking in terms of more physically realistic vibrational frequency spectra than that considered in Section 3.1. If we begin by assuming that all the particles are vibrating with the same frequency v, then γ gives the volume variation of this frequency as

$$\gamma = -d(\ln v)/d(\ln V)$$

In fact, we know that a range of frequencies exists, and we may think in terms of a frequency distribution function $f(v)$ defining the number of normal modes of vibration per unit frequency range, corresponding to each frequency v_j in which we may associate a particular value of γ, denoted by γ_j. One of the major tasks of the theoretician is to sum these values of γ_j over the spectrum to give $\gamma = \Sigma \gamma_j$ on the basis of the assumptions within some theoretical model. According to the quasiharmonic approach γ is a weighted average of the γ_j, the weight for each normal mode being its contribution to C_V. It follows that a temperature variation of γ is to be expected, with low- and high-temperature limiting values given by

$$\gamma_0 = - \, d(\ln \theta_0)/d(\ln V) \quad \text{and} \quad \gamma_\infty = \left(\sum_{j=1}^{3\mathcal{N}} \gamma_j\right)\Big/3\mathcal{N}$$

respectively, in which θ_0 is the low-temperature limiting value of the Debye characteristic temperature and $\mathcal{N}$ is the number of vibrating particles in the assembly. The numerical values of γ_0 and γ_∞ and the temperature variation of γ between these two limits, calculated according to the assumptions of some theoretical model, may be compared with the results for real solids by expressing γ in terms of physically measurable quantities:

$$\gamma = \beta V/C_V \chi_T = \beta V/C_P \chi_S$$

which expresses Eqs. (3.12) and (3.13). Comparing these equations with the thermodynamic equation

$$\beta/\chi_T = (\partial S/\partial V)_T$$

Barron (1955) has expressed γ in the general form

$$\gamma = \sum_{j=1}^{3\mathcal{N}} \gamma_j \frac{(h\nu_j/kT)^2 \, e^{h\nu_j/kT}}{(e^{h\nu_j/kT} - 1)^2} \Big/ \sum_{j=1}^{3\mathcal{N}} \frac{(h\nu_j/kT)^2 \, e^{h\nu_j/kT}}{(e^{h\nu_j/kT} - 1)^2} \tag{5.2}$$

in which the component terms have their usual meanings.

Among the most successful applications of the quasiharmonic approach to thermodynamic problems, that expounded by Barron et al. (1957) deserves special mention. Later works have produced refinements and extensions of their techniques, but the broad principles of approach remain essentially unchanged.

5.5. THE TEMPERATURE DEPENDENCE OF THE DEBYE CHARACTERISTIC TEMPERATURE

Because of the convergence of different mathematical series expansions, it is convenient to consider the temperature range in three sections.

5.5.1. The Low-Temperature Region

It may be shown fairly easily that to a good approximation the Debye temperatures of a cubic solid may be corrected for volume change

$$\theta(V_0)/\theta(V) \approx (V/V_0)^\gamma \tag{5.3}$$

in which the terms have their usual meanings. In order to determine $\theta(V)$, it is first necessary to calculate C_V. Before this may be done any additional contributions to the heat capacity, such as the electronic contribution in the case of a metal or an alloy, must be subtracted. The Grüneisen parameter may then be calculated from Eq. (3.13). At this stage of the analysis the most appropriate value of γ required for the volume correction, γ_∞, may be estimated by extrapolating a plot of γ against a rapidly converging function of temperature to $T = \infty$. Such a function has been defined by Barron *et al.* (1964):

$$t = \frac{1}{1 + (T/0.2\theta_\infty)^2} \tag{5.4}$$

and extrapolation of γ to $t = 0$ yields a value of γ_∞. This value of γ is used in Eq. (5.2) to correct $\theta(V)$ to $\theta(V_0)$.

It is well established that at very low temperatures the specific heat of a dielectric solid may be represented by the equation

$$C_V = aT^3 + bT^5 + cT^7 + \cdots \tag{5.5}$$

in which a, b, c, etc. are constants. We saw earlier that at very low temperatures the Debye approximation holds. This corresponds to the first term above, and for $T < \theta/12$

$$C_V = (4\pi^4/5)3\mathscr{N}k(T/\theta)^3 \tag{5.6}$$

to an accuracy of approximately 1%. A graph of C_V/T^3 against T^2 may therefore be expected to give θ_0, the low-temperature limiting value of the Debye characteristic temperature, from the intercept at $T^2 = 0$. We saw in Section 3.4 that θ_0 might also be calculated from the low-temperature elastic constants, thus providing a means of correlating low-temperature calorimetric and elasticity data.

The expansion for the frequency spectrum at low temperatures is

$$f(v) = \mathscr{N}(\alpha v^2 + \beta v^4 + \gamma v^6 + \cdots) \tag{5.7}$$

in which the coefficients α, β, γ, etc. are directly related to a, b, c, etc. in Eq. (5.5). Thus the graph of C_V/T^3 versus T^2 gives estimates of b and c provided that the low-temperature heat capacity data from which they are derived are very precise, and these coefficients give some information about the form of the frequency spectrum at low frequencies.

At this stage we have derived $\theta(V_0)$ as a function of temperature.

5.5.2. The High-Temperature Region

The specific heat of a dielectric solid at high temperatures can be expressed in the form of a series (Thirring, 1913):

$$C_V = 3 \mathcal{N} k \left(1 - \frac{B_2}{2!} \frac{\mu_2{}^*}{T^2} + \frac{3B_4}{4!} \frac{\mu_4{}^*}{T^4} - \frac{5B_6}{6!} \frac{\mu_6{}^*}{T^6} + \cdots \right) \qquad (5.8)$$

in which

$$\mu_n{}^* = (h/k)^n \overline{\nu^n} \qquad \text{and} \qquad \overline{\nu^n} = \int_0^\infty \nu^n f(\nu)\, d\nu \Big/ \int_0^\infty f(\nu)\, d\nu \qquad (5.9)$$

and B_n are the Bernoulli numbers, $B_2 = 1/6$, $B_4 = 1/30$, $B_6 = 1/42$, etc. $\overline{\nu^n}$ is called the nth moment of frequency ν. Unfortunately, Eq. (5.8) converges rapidly only above $T \approx \theta_\infty/2$, at which temperature anharmonic effects are generally becoming rather serious. The equivalent expansion in terms of θ converges at lower temperatures, however (Domb and Salter, 1952):

$$\theta^2 = \theta_\infty^2 [1 - A(\theta_\infty/T)^2 + B(\theta_\infty/T)^4 - \cdots] \qquad (5.10)$$

in which

$$\theta_\infty = (h/k)(5\overline{\nu^2}/3)^{1/2} \qquad (5.11)$$

$$A = (3/100)\{[\overline{\nu^4}/(\overline{\nu^2})^2] - (25/21)\} \qquad (5.12)$$

and

$$B = (1/1400)\{[\overline{\nu^6}/(\overline{\nu^2})^3] - (125/81) - 100A\} \qquad (5.13)$$

In order to determine the positive, even moments $\overline{\nu^2}$, $\overline{\nu^4}$, and $\overline{\nu^6}$, the harmonic value of $\theta_\infty(V_0)$ may first be estimated on the basis of Eq. (5.10) by plotting a graph of $[\theta(V_0)]^2$ versus T^{-2}, and extrapolating from the approximate temperature region $\theta_\infty/6 < T < \theta_\infty/3$ to $T^{-2} = 0$. The reason for choosing this particular range is that Eq. (5.10) cannot be expected to hold at temperatures below approximately $\theta_\infty/6$, while anharmonic effects usually start to get quite serious at approximately, $\theta_\infty/3$. {In fact, an earlier plot of the uncorrected $[\theta(V)]^2$ against T^{-2} would have been made to get a first estimate of θ_∞, required for the determination of t in Eq. (5.4).} The value of $\theta_\infty(V_0)$ derived above may be used to calculate $\overline{\nu^2}$ from Eq. (5.11). We may determine the coefficients A and B of Eq. (5.10) by rearranging the terms and extrapolating a graph of $\{1 - [\theta(V_0)/\theta_\infty(V_0)]^2\}/[\theta_\infty(V_0)/T]^2$ against $[\theta_\infty(V_0)/T]^2$ from the same temperature region as before, to get the intercept and gradient. Knowing A and B, $\overline{\nu^4}$ and $\overline{\nu^6}$ may then be calculated from Eqs. (5.12) and (5.13).

5.5.3. The Intermediate-Temperature Region

Salter (1955) drew attention to the way in which the geometric mean frequency v_g of the vibrational spectrum, defined by

$$v_g = \left(\prod_{j=1}^{3\mathcal{N}} v_j \right)^{1/3\mathcal{N}}$$

might be calculated from the high-temperature entropy S. The two are related by the equation

$$S = 3\mathcal{N}k\left(1 - \ln \frac{hv_g}{kT} + \frac{B_2}{2 \cdot 2!} \frac{\mu_2{}^*}{T^2} \right.$$
$$\left. - \frac{3B_4}{4 \cdot 4!} \frac{\mu_4{}^*}{T^4} + \frac{5B_6}{6 \cdot 6!} \frac{\mu_6{}^*}{T^6} - \cdots \right) \qquad (5.14)$$

In using this equation to evaluate the "harmonic entropy," the "harmonic heat capacity" is used, after reduction to the volume at 0°K. Furthermore, the summations are evaluated at the lowest temperature τ for which terms beyond that in T^{-6} become negligible. This same restriction is imposed in calculating the first moment $\overline{v^1}$ from the equation

$$\frac{3}{2}\mathcal{N}\,h\overline{v^1} = 3\mathcal{N}kT\left(1 + \frac{B_2}{2!} \frac{\mu_2{}^*}{\tau^2} - \frac{B_4}{4!} \frac{\mu_4{}^*}{\tau^4} + \frac{B_6}{6!} \frac{\mu_6{}^*}{\tau^6} - \cdots \right)$$
$$- \int_0^\tau C_{\text{har}}\, dT \qquad (5.15)$$

given by Barron et al. (1957). Integrating the Thirring expansion for C_V/T^n and using an expression derived by Hwang (1954), Barron et al. (1957) have also derived the expression

$$\overline{v^{1-n}} = \frac{1}{\Gamma(n+1)\zeta(n)} \left(\frac{h}{k} \right)^{n-1} \left[\frac{1}{3\mathcal{N}k} \int_0^\tau \frac{C_{\text{har}}}{T^n}\, dT + \frac{1}{n-1} \frac{1}{\tau^{n-1}} \right.$$
$$\left. - \sum_{s=1}^{\infty} (-1)^{s+1} \frac{B_{2s}}{(2s)!} \frac{2s-1}{2s+n-1} \left(\frac{h}{k} \right)^{2s} \frac{\overline{v^{2s}}}{\tau^{2s+n-1}} \right]$$
$$1 < n < 4 \qquad (5.16)$$

in which B_{2s} are the Bernoulli numbers, defined earlier, $\Gamma(n+1)$ is the gamma function, and $\zeta(n)$ is the Riemann zeta function. Again the expressions are evaluated at the lowest temperatures for which terms beyond those in T^{-6} become negligible.

5.6. REPRESENTATION OF THE MOMENTS
AND THEIR INTERPRETATION

Substituting a function of the form $f(v) = cv^2$ for the distribution function in Eq. (5.9), in which c is a constant, and evaluating the integrals up to the cutoff frequency of the equivalent Debye distribution, we obtain an explicit expression for the maximum frequency $v_D(n)$ of the Debye distribution having the same nth moment as the vibrational frequency spectrum in the actual crystal. Thus, for $n > -3$

$$v_D(n) = [\tfrac{1}{3}(n + 3)\overline{v^n}]^{1/n} \qquad (n \neq 0) \tag{5.17}$$

This equation may be used to calculate $v_D(n)$ for $n = -2, -1, 1, 2, 4, 6$ from the moments calculated so far. Additional values of $v_D(n)$ for $n = -3$ and 0 may be calculated from

$$v_D(-3) = k\theta_0/h \qquad \text{and} \qquad v_D(0) = e^{1/3}v_g \tag{5.18}$$

using the values of θ_0 and v_g derived earlier.

Typical values of $v_D(n)$ as functions of n are shown in Fig. 28. The dependence of $v_D(n)$ upon n gives a measure of the departure of the true frequency spectrum from the Debye form, and the existence of systematic trends is clearly evident in graphs of this kind. In particular, we may note in this case that as the mass of the positive ion increases: (a) $v_D(n)$ diminishes for a given value of n, (b) $v_D(n)$ passes through minima at increasingly negative values of n, and (c) the overall variation of $v_D(n)$ with n increases. Examination of corresponding results among the sodium and potassium halides, which have the rocksalt structure, leads to similar conclusions. If we look next at the effect of increasing the mass of the halide ion for a particular alkali ion, we find a similar reduction of $v_D(n)$ with n, but the quantitative effect is much less, suggesting the predominance of the alkali ion in determining interionic forces in ionic solids. It may be recalled that observations on the Grüneisen parameters led to the same conclusion. Supporting evidence comes from the alkali halides possessing the cesium chloride structure, for which data are less numerous, though a continuous quantitative comparison of moments among the alkali halides is not possible because of the two crystal structures (Kirkham and Yates, 1968). If we look at graphs of $v_D(n)$ against n for alkali halides having both the rocksalt structure and the cesium chloride structure shown by Kirkham and Yates, we find that the variations of $v_D(n)$ with n in both series diminish as the ratio of the constituent masses of the molecules approach unity. This suggests that the

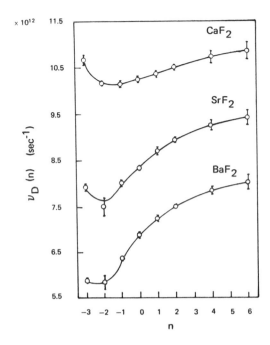

Fig. 28. The function $\nu_D(n)$ as a function of n for calcium fluoride, strontium fluoride, and barium fluoride, in which the uncertainties are indicated by the vertical lines (after Bailey and Yates, 1967*b*).

harmonic frequency spectra corresponding to the actual spectra approximate more closely to the Debye form at the higher frequencies as the masses of the constituent ions become more nearly equal. This empirical observation is consistent with the results of calculations performed by Karo (1959, 1960), who showed how the acoustic and optical branches of spectra of alkali halides with the rocksalt structure gradually separated for large mass ratios, until a definite gap appeared. For NaF, KCl, and RbBr, however, there was maximum overlap of the longitudinal acoustic and the transverse optical branches, resulting in characteristically high central peaks in the spectra of the face-centered cubic alkali halides having mass ratios closest to unity. Corresponding results for pyrolytic graphite, which is hexagonal, contain two differences from the foregoing results which stand out in comparison: (a) the spread in values among the $\nu_D(n)$ in the range $-3 \leq n \leq 6$ is considerably greater in the case of graphite, and (b) no minimum in $\nu_D(n)$ occurs within this range of n (see Bailey and Yates, 1969). From these observations it is clear that the actual vibrational frequency spectrum of graphite must be particularly complex.

It would obviously be desirable to extend thermodynamic data currently available for more complex solids in order to look for patterns, in view of the way in which these have emerged from studies of alkali halides, for which the available data appear to be most comprehensive at the present time. Comparison of the patterns emerging from the systems might usefully be made in order to examine the influences of (1) crystal structure, (2) the nature of the bonding, and (3) the mass ratio upon (a) the temperature dependence of the variation of the frequencies of lattice vibrations with volume, and (b) the variation with order of the maximum frequency of the Debye distribution having the same moment as the frequency spectrum in an actual crystal possessing the same order of moment.

Summarizing some immediate applications of the moments of the frequency distribution of a solid, through the representation afforded by maximum frequencies of the equivalent Debye distributions,

$$\theta_0^C = \theta_0^S = (h/k)\nu_D(-3) \tag{5.19}$$

$$\theta_\infty^C = (h/k)\nu_D(2) \tag{5.20}$$

and

$$\theta_\infty^S = (h/k)\nu_D(0) \tag{5.21}$$

in which the superscripts C and S refer to specific heat and entropy, respectively, as before. The limiting characteristic temperatures representing the Debye–Waller exponent M for a simple crystal are given by

$$\theta_0^M = (h/k)\nu_D(1) \tag{5.22}$$

and

$$\theta_\infty^M = (h/k)\nu_D(-2) \tag{5.23}$$

Incidentally, this parameter, which provides a measure of the temperature variation of the intensity of Bragg reflections of X-rays or neutrons from crystals, may be calculated as a function of temperature using good thermodynamic data more precisely than it can be obtained directly [see, e.g., Yates (1966) and Brade and Yates (1969)]. The first moment of a crystal may be used to calculate the zero-point energy E_z from

$$E_z = \tfrac{3}{2}\mathcal{N}\,h\overline{\nu^1} \tag{5.24}$$

and it is of some interest to compare the ratio of the zero-point energy to the thermal energy of a crystal with the corresponding ratio for a related crystal at a common reduced temperature in order to try to get some ideas concerning the onset of anharmonicity. Finally, the moments may be employed in calculating the temperature dependence of the root mean square amplitudes of vibration of atoms in solids as functions of temperature. Employing expressions deduced by Blackman (1956) and Barron *et al.* (1963), Leadbetter (1965) has shown that the root mean square amplitudes of vibration $\overline{u^2}$ at the absolute zero of temperature may be obtained directly from the first moment $\overline{\nu^1}$ through the equation

$$m\overline{u^2} = h\overline{\nu^1}/8\pi^2 \tag{5.25}$$

in which m is the average mass of a vibrating unit. At higher temperatures, i.e., when $T > \theta/2\pi$

$$m\overline{u^2} = \frac{kT}{4\pi^2}\left[\overline{\nu^{-2}} + \frac{B_2}{2!}\left(\frac{h}{kT}\right)^2 - \frac{B_4}{4!}\left(\frac{h}{kT}\right)^4\overline{\nu^2} + \cdots\right] \tag{5.26}$$

5.7. THE VOLUME DEPENDENCE OF THE MOMENTS

Just as the heat capacity of a solid gave us information concerning the moments of the frequency distribution of the atomic vibrations and the coefficients in the low-frequency expansion, so, in principle at any rate, thermal expansion gives information concerning the volume variation of these quantities. The volume dependence of the moments may be expressed conveniently in the form

$$\gamma(n) = \frac{\sum_{j=1}^{3\mathcal{N}}\gamma_j\nu_j^n}{\sum_{j=1}^{3\mathcal{N}}\nu_j^n} = -\frac{1}{n}\frac{d(\ln\nu^n)}{d(\ln V)} = \frac{d[\ln\nu_D(n)]}{d(\ln V)} \tag{5.27}$$

Again it will be convenient to consider the temperature range in three main areas.

5.7.1. The Low-Temperature Region

Since $\beta/\chi_T = (\partial S/\partial V)_T$ and $\gamma = \beta V/C_V\chi_T$, it follows that we may express the Grüneisen parameter as

$$\gamma = (V/C_V)(\partial S/\partial V)_T \tag{5.28}$$

From Eq. (5.5)

$$C_V = aT^3 + bT^5 + cT^7 + \cdots$$

Integrating C_V/T against T to get the low-temperature entropy and making the appropriate substitutions, it follows that

$$\gamma = \frac{1}{3}\frac{d(\ln a)}{d(\ln V)} + \frac{b}{a}\, T^2\left[\frac{1}{5}\frac{d(\ln b)}{d(\ln V)} - \frac{1}{3}\frac{d(\ln a)}{d(\ln V)}\right] + \cdots$$

In principle, therefore, a plot of γ against T^2 at low temperatures should yield

$$\gamma_0 = \tfrac{1}{3}d(\ln a)/d(\ln V)$$

from the intercept and

$$\tfrac{1}{5}\,d(\ln b)/d(\ln V)$$

from the slope at $T^2 = 0$. In practice, the experimental accuracy of thermal expansion measurements in the neighborhood of $T = 0$ is not sufficiently high to allow either a or b to be estimated in this way. If high-precision data on low-temperature specific heat, thermal expansion, and elastic constants exist, γ_0 may be obtained by extrapolating to $T = 0$, as may be seen in Fig. 29. The existence of all these data to a high degree of precision down to very low temperatures is unusual, however, and it is more usual to have to estimate γ_0 by a crude extrapolation from intermediate temperatures. This is most unsatisfactory, and a much more reliable evaluation of γ_0 may be effected from measurements of the pressure dependence of the elastic constants, preferably determined at a low temperature. Reverting to our new notation, we may note that

$$\gamma_0 \equiv \gamma(-3) \tag{5.29}$$

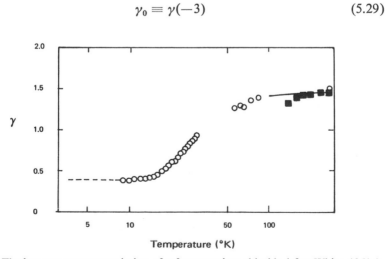

Fig. 29.   The low-temperature variation of γ for potassium chloride (after White, 1961c).

5.7.2. The High-Temperature Region

We saw earlier that according to the quasiharmonic approximation γ was a weighted average of the γ_j, the weight for each normal mode being its contribution to C_V. Expanding Eq. (5.1) Barron (1955) produced a result which may be expressed in the form

$$\gamma = \gamma(0) - T^{-2}\left\{\frac{\mu_2{}^*}{12}\,[\gamma(2) - \gamma(0)]\right\} + T^{-4}\left\{\frac{\mu_4{}^*}{240}\,[\gamma(4) - \gamma(0)]\right.$$

$$- \left(\frac{\mu_2{}^*}{12}\right)^2 [\gamma(2) - \gamma(0)]\right\} - T^{-6}\left\{\frac{\mu_6{}^*}{6048}\,[\gamma(6) - \gamma(0)]\right.$$

$$- \frac{\mu_2{}^*}{12}\frac{\mu_4{}^*}{240}\,[\gamma(4) - \gamma(0)]$$

$$+ \frac{\mu_2{}^*}{12}\left[\left(\frac{\mu_2{}^*}{12}\right)^2 - \frac{\mu_4{}^*}{240}\right][\gamma(2) - \gamma(0)]\right\} + \cdots \qquad (5.30)$$

where $\gamma(n)$ is defined in Eq. (5.27). The first and second differential coefficients of a plot of $(\gamma_\infty - \gamma)T^2$ against T^{-2} thus yield $\gamma(2)$, $\gamma(4)$, and $\gamma(6)$. In practice, more rapid convergence of Eq. (5.30) may be obtained by transforming the variable from T to t defined in Eq. (5.4), as was done in estimating γ_∞ for the volume correction to $\theta(V)$. Again we may note that in accordance with the new notation we may write

$$\gamma_\infty \equiv \gamma(0) \qquad (5.31)$$

5.7.3. The Intermediate-Temperature Region

We now require $\gamma(-1)$ and $\gamma(-2)$. The equations with the aid of which these quantities may be calculated, using the quasiharmonic approximation, are

$$\gamma(n) = \int_0^\infty \gamma C_{\text{har}} T^{n-1}\,dT \Big/ \int_0^\infty C_{\text{har}} T^{n-1}\,dT, \qquad -3 < n < 0 \quad (5.32)$$

In employing the value of C_{har} estimated from the experimentally measured C_V, it will be remembered that we derived these quantities by correcting θ to a fixed volume (that corresponding to $0°$K), and that we extrapolated the results from the approximate temperature range $\theta_\infty/6 < T < \theta_\infty/3$ to $T = \infty$ in attempting to estimate θ_{har} and hence C_{har}. In so doing we attempted to allow for the effect of volume change upon C_V, but it should be recalled that we have not allowed for the volume dependence of γ, or for constant-volume, temperature-dependent anharmonic effects.

Both of these effects are likely to be small at all but the highest temperatures.

We now have $\gamma(n)$ for values of n lying between -3 and $+6$. It will be relevant to look briefly at the applications of these quantities and at their physical interpretation. We have just recalled one instance in which it was necessary to correct a characteristic temperature for volume change. This was the Debye temperature corresponding to the representation of specific heat. There are other instances of this requirement, and for each a different value of $\gamma(n)$ is most appropriate. Using the same notation as previously, we may note the following three volume-correction relationships:

$$\theta^C(V_0)/\theta^C(V) \approx (V/V_0)^{\gamma(2)} \tag{5.33}$$

$$\theta^S(V_0)/\theta^S(V) \approx (V/V_0)^{\gamma(0)} \tag{5.34}$$

$$\theta^M(V_0)/\theta^M(V) \approx (V/V_0)^{\gamma(-2)} \tag{5.35}$$

In the θ^C volume correction, $\gamma(0)$ was used in place of $\gamma(2)$ in Eq. (5.3). The use of $\gamma(2)$ would have involved presupposing the outcome of subsequent calculations, and the error resulting from this approximation is generally much smaller than the experimental uncertainties, because of the numerical similarity of $\gamma(0)$ and $\gamma(2)$. In the interests of simplicity, the mathematics of the foregoing descriptions has been restricted to a form appropriate to solids possessing cubic symmetry. Barron and Munn (1967) have extended the notation and the concepts behind these ideas to cover cases of reduced symmetry, and in looking at the physical interpretations to be put upon the moments and their variations with volume, it will be instructive to extend our considerations to include cases of anisotropic solids. Results of calculations of the volume dependences of the moments are not as common as those of the moments themselves, though the results that do exist are particularly interesting, correlating closely with known properties of the crystals. Differences between the forms of the variations of $\gamma(n)$ with n from one crystal form to another are much greater than the differences observed in the corresponding graphs of $\nu_D(n)$ against n.

Figure 30 shows two typical curves of this type. Examining the characteristics of Fig. 30(b) and considering first $\gamma_\parallel(n)$, we note that this is fairly large and positive when $n = -3$, whereas $\gamma_\perp(n)$ is quite large and negative. It will be recalled that $\gamma(-3) \equiv \gamma_0$, and so we may expect the behavior corresponding to $n = -3$ to be essentially low-temperature behavior, which will be dominated by the low-frequency modes. The inference is that the volume dependence of the low-frequency modes in the c crystallographic axis direc-

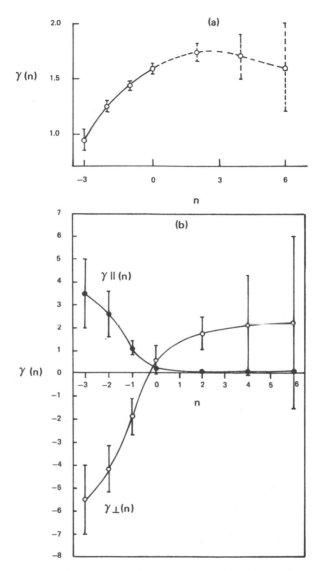

Fig. 30. The volume dependences of the moments $\gamma(n)$ of (a) sodium chloride (after Barron *et al.*, 1964) and (b) pyrolytic graphite (after Bailey and Yates, 1969), as functions of *n*.

tion of pyrolytic graphite is high, and we may therefore expect the density of low-frequency modes of vibration to be high in this crystalline direction. The negative value of $\gamma_\perp(-3)$ indicates the predominance of transverse modes of vibration among the vibrations within the *a–a* plane. When

$n \geq 0$, on the other hand, we have a contribution from the vibrations at high temperatures, at which the higher-frequency modes of vibration will be excited. The low value of $\gamma_{\parallel}(n)$ in this region points to the scarcity of high-frequency modes in the interplanar vibrations, while the increasingly large and positive values of $\gamma_{\perp}(n)$ are consistent with the existence of a high density of high-frequency longitudinal vibrations within the planes perpendicular to the c crystallographic axis. By analogy with a simple, vibrating mechanical system one may associate low-frequency modes with weak binding forces, and high-frequency modes with strong binding forces. We are therefore left to expect pyrolytic graphite to have strong binding forces between the atoms within the a–a planes, and weak forces between the planes. This corresponds with our knowledge of the structure and properties of the substance based upon information from alternative sources.

Chapter 6

The Quantitative Study of Anharmonic Effects

6.1. THE IDENTIFICATION OF AN EXPLICIT TEMPERATURE DEPENDENCE OF THE VIBRATIONAL FREQUENCIES

We saw earlier that it was possible to represent the potential energy of of a crystal lattice by a series expansion in which the higher-order terms represented deviations from harmonic behavior. A sudden onset of anharmonic effects would be out of keeping with our experience of natural phenomena, and so we may reasonably expect these to occur down to $T = 0°K$, at which temperature the effect would be associated with the zero-point vibrations (Leibfried and Ludwig, 1961; Barron, 1964). Being very small below approximately $T = \theta°K$, they are very difficult to study at low temperatures, however. We have seen that experience based upon the analysis of experimental data up to approximately $\theta_\infty/3$ has produced self-consistent results which accord with the idea of anharmonic effects being relatively unimportant below this temperature. We have also seen that for the treatment of data up to $T \approx \theta°K$ adequate account of anharmonicity was taken by allowing for the volume dependence of the frequencies, which were assumed to remain harmonic in character. At somewhat higher temperatures, however, it becomes necessary to allow for an explicit temperature dependence of the frequencies at constant volume. Attempts have been made to investigate the occurrence of anharmonicity quantitatively using low-temperature data of high precision (e.g., Tosi and Fumi, 1963; Leadbetter, 1965; Overton, 1962, 1966). The main objection to approaches along these lines is that it is necessary to make some assumptions about the form of the temperature dependence. For example, Tosi and Fumi (1963) assumed that the leading term in the expression for the temperature-dependent anharmonic contribution to the heat capacity was proportional to T, while Leadbetter (1965) assumed that anharmonic frequency shifts were proportional to the energy content of the crystal. A simpler dependence upon temperature is expected at high temperatures, although high-precision data do not exist in great abundance at these temperatures. A further complication inherent in the high-temperature data arises because of the possibility of vacancy formation in those solids for which large gaps do not exist between the Debye temperature and the melting point. Serious efforts to overcome these deficiencies of data have been made recently by Leadbetter and co-workers (1968, 1969).

First-order quantum mechanical perturbation theory predicts that the constant-volume anharmonic contributions to the heat capacity and entropy are directly proportional to temperature at high temperatures, i.e.,

$$\Delta C_V^{\text{anh}} = \Delta S^{\text{anh}} = AT \tag{6.1}$$

where A is a constant. Direct estimates of these explicitly temperature-dependent contributions may be made by correcting experimentally based Debye temperatures for the effect of volume change using the fixed-volume moments and their volume derivatives using Eq. (5.19), (5.20), and (5.33). Subtracting these values from values of C_V based upon experimental observation then yields values of ΔC_V^{anh} directly. The reasoning behind the analytical procedure adopted in specific instances is outlined below.

6.2. GENERAL CONSIDERATIONS

Treating anharmonicity as a perturbation, the Helmholtz free energy may be written as

$$F(T, V) = F^{\text{qh}}(T, V) + \Delta F^{\text{anh}}(T, V) \tag{6.2}$$

in which the quasiharmonic contribution F^{qh} contains the contribution due to $\phi_2(V)$ in Eq. (5.1), and ΔF^{anh} is the explicit anharmonic contribution, containing the contribution from all the other terms in the expansion. It is convenient to transform Eq. (6.2) to the first and second derivatives of F, which are more sensitive to the detailed nature of the vibrations, as well as being more directly experimentally accessible. Adopting analogous representations, we may write

$$S(T, V) = S^{\text{qh}}(T, V) + \Delta S^{\text{anh}}(T, V) \tag{6.3}$$

and

$$C_V(T, V) = C_V^{qh}(T, V) + \Delta C_V^{anh}(T, V) \qquad (6.4)$$

The terms on the right-hand sides of these equations correspond to those in the right-hand side of Eq. (6.2). Leadbetter (1968b) has shown that the general theory of crystal anharmonicity leads to the result

$$\Delta F^{anh}(T, V)/3\mathcal{N}k = K(V) - \tfrac{1}{2}A(V)T^2 - \tfrac{1}{3}B(V)T^3 - \cdots \qquad (6.5)$$

from which it follows that we may write

$$\begin{aligned}\Delta S^{anh}(T, V)/3\mathcal{N}k &= -[\partial(\Delta F^{anh})/\partial T]_V \\ &= A(V)T + B(V)T^2 + C(V)T^3 + \cdots \end{aligned} \qquad (6.6)$$

and

$$\begin{aligned}\Delta C^{anh}(T, V)/3\mathcal{N}k &= -T[\partial^2(\Delta F^{anh})/\partial T^2)]_V \\ &= A(V)T + 2B(V)T^2 + 3C(V)T^3 + \cdots \end{aligned} \qquad (6.7)$$

In these equations $A(V)$, $B(V)$, and $C(V)$ are the first, second, and third anharmonic coefficients, respectively, and $K(V)$ is a function of volume only.

We saw earlier that γ was the weighted average of the various values of γ_j, the weight for each normal mode being its contribution to C_V, i.e.,

$$\gamma = \left(\sum_{j=1}^{n} \gamma_j C_j \right) \Big/ C_V$$

in which C_j is the contribution to the specific heat from the jth normal mode. Expressing the entropy as the simple sum of n independent contributions, i.e., $S = \sum_{j=1} S_j$, it follows that γ_j takes the form

$$\gamma_j = (1/C_j)[\partial S_j/\partial(\ln V)]_T$$

This being so, it follows from Eq. (6.6) and (6.7) that we may write

$$\gamma C_V = \gamma^{qh} C_V^{qh} + \gamma^{anh} C_V^{anh} \qquad (6.8)$$

in which

$$\gamma^{anh} = (1/\Delta C_V^{anh})[\partial(\Delta S^{anh})/\partial(\ln V)]_T$$

Having expressed the entropy, heat capacity, and Grüneisen parameter in the form of sums of a quasiharmonic contribution and an explicitly temperature-dependent anharmonic contribution, the next tasks will be to determine these two components separately.

6.3. THE QUASIHARMONIC COMPONENTS OF THE SPECIFIC HEAT, ENTROPY, AND GRÜNEISEN PARAMETER

We saw in Section 5.5 that the quasiharmonic contribution to the heat capacity at elevated temperatures could be estimated from a suitable extrapolation of data taken at temperatures below approximately $\theta_\infty/3$. In this process, use was made of Eq. (5.10). Including the superscript C to denote specific heat, we have

$$(\theta^C)^2 = (\theta_\infty^C)^2[1 - A(\theta_\infty^C/T)^2 + B(\theta_\infty^C/T)^4 - \cdots]$$

Similarly, we may write

$$\theta^S = \theta_\infty^S[1 + (L/T^2) + (M/T^4) + \cdots] \tag{6.9}$$

corresponding to the entropy, and

$$\gamma = \gamma_\infty[1 + (P/T^2) + (Q/T^4) + \cdots] \tag{6.10}$$

which corresponds to Eq. (5.30). In these equations L, M, P, Q, etc. are constants. It is to be understood that the subjects of these equations are the quasiharmonic values, and it may be recalled that θ_∞^C and θ_∞^S were defined in terms of the moments in Eqs. (5.20) and (5.21). In reducing the data to fixed volume one may express

$$d(\ln \gamma)/d(\ln V) = Y$$

in which γ is ideally the quasiharmonic value of γ. In practice, only the experimental value of γ is available in the first instance, though this should provide a reasonable approximation. Integrating, we have

$$\gamma(V)/\gamma(V_0) = (V/V_0)^Y \tag{6.11}$$

Employing purely thermodynamic arguments, Barron et al. (1964) have obtained an expression for Y which may be expressed in the form

$$Y = 1 - \frac{\chi_T}{\beta}\left(\frac{\partial K_T}{\partial T}\right)_P - \frac{T}{C_P\chi_T}\left[\frac{\partial(\beta V)}{\partial T}\right]_P - \frac{\chi_S}{\chi_T}\left(\frac{\partial K_S}{\partial P}\right)_T \tag{6.12}$$

All the quantities on the right-hand side are experimentally attainable, permitting an evaluation of Y, and hence $\gamma(V_0)$ may be determined from Eq. (6.11). Plotting this value of $\gamma(V_0)$ against T^{-2} or, better still, the parameter t defined in Eq. (5.4) permits the estimation of P, Q, and R in Eq. (6.10), and hence of $\gamma(2)$, $\gamma(4)$, and $\gamma(6)$ in Eq. (5.30). The value of $\gamma(2)$

so derived may be applied in Eq. (5.33) to correct the characteristic temperature θ^C to constant volume in order to allow for the effect of thermal expansion. The use of $\gamma(0)$, described earlier, is justified on grounds of convenience in the determination of moments, but the more precise use of $\gamma(2)$ is preferable when studying anharmonic effects quantitatively, because of the small fraction of the total heat capacity having its origin in these effects. However, the insensitivity of C_V to θ^C above temperatures of approximately $\theta^C_\infty/2$ makes it unnecessary to go to the extreme of correcting $\gamma(2)$ to the quasiharmonic value. For the same reason the volume dependence of $\gamma(2)$ may also be ignored. Extrapolation of these corrected values of θ^C, within the quasiharmonic approximation, to give quasiharmonic values at elevated temperatures then follows the procedure described in Chapter 5.

The entropy is much more sensitive to its characteristic temperature than is the specific heat, and for this reason the value of $\gamma(0)$ used in correcting $\theta^S(V)$ for the effect of thermal expansion using Eq. (5.34) must be the quasiharmonic value, corrected to constant volume. By analogy with Y, defined earlier, we may define

$$d(\ln \gamma^{qh}_\infty)/d(\ln V) = Y'$$

which may be used together with the differential form of Eq. (5.34) applied to quasiharmonic values to express the volume variation of the quasiharmonic value of the characteristic temperature corresponding to the entropy in the form

$$\ln\left[\frac{\theta^S_{qh}(T, V_0)}{\theta^S_{qh}(T, V)}\right] = \gamma^{qh}_\infty(V_0)\frac{\Delta V}{V_0}\left[1 + \frac{1}{2}(Y' - 1)\frac{\Delta V}{V_0} + \cdots\right] \quad (6.13)$$

in which $\Delta V = V - V_0$. Y' is not obtainable directly from experiment, nor is Y usually available as a function of temperature. In practice, however, the difference between Y and Y' is likely to be small, and the degree of dependence upon temperature is likely to be low, and so Y may be used for Y' in describing the volume dependence of γ^{qh} with confidence.

The steps in the detailed procedure by which the explicit anharmonic contributions to the heat capacity and entropy are assessed will be summarized later. Meanwhile the foregoing description indicates the main steps in the extrapolation of the low-temperature data, which contain only a very small proportion of anharmonic effects, in the estimation of the quasiharmonic contribution to the heat capacity and entropy at elevated temperatures.

6.4. THE EXPLICIT ANHARMONIC COMPONENTS OF
THE SPECIFIC HEAT, ENTROPY, AND GRÜNEISEN PARAMETER

Leadbetter (1968c) has drawn attention to the potential value of calculating the explicit anharmonic contributions to the specific heat, entropy, and Grüneisen parameter by two different approaches in order to afford a check on the numerical work and on the self-consistency of the assumptions made in the treatments. One may estimate the quasiharmonic values of these three quantities by the procedure described above and then subtract these from the measured values to yield the explicit anharmonic contributions in accordance with Eqs. (6.3), (6.4), and (6.8). The values of $\Delta S^{\mathrm{anh}}(V)$ and $\Delta C_V^{\mathrm{anh}}(V)$ so obtained may then be corrected for volume change to a good approximation using γ^{anh}, giving the explicit anharmonic contribution at V_0. Alternatively, it is possible to evaluate the temperature dependence of $\Delta S^{\mathrm{anh}}(V_0)$ and $\Delta C_V^{\mathrm{anh}}(V_0)$ directly by subtracting the fixed-volume quasiharmonic contributions from the experimental quantities, after these have first been corrected to the values corresponding to V_0 using thermodynamic relations.

Pursuing this latter approach, it may be shown that

$$\left\{\frac{\partial[\ln(\beta/\chi_T)]}{\partial(\ln V)}\right\}_T = -\frac{\chi_T}{\beta}\left(\frac{\partial K_T}{\partial T}\right)_P - \left(\frac{\partial K_T}{\partial P}\right)_T = X, \quad \text{say} \quad (6.14)$$

Employing a result derived by Overton (1962) and making use of Eq. (6.12) defining Y, one may express Y in terms of X through the equation

$$Y = X + 1 - \frac{T}{\chi_T C_P}\left(\frac{\partial(\beta V)}{\partial T}\right)_P + \left(\frac{\partial K_T}{\partial P}\right)_T - \frac{\chi_S}{\chi_T}\left(\frac{\partial K_S}{\partial P}\right)_T \quad (6.15)$$

(cf. Settatree, 1968). Leadbetter (1968c) has employed the thermodynamic relationship $(\partial S/\partial V)_T = \beta/\chi_T$ to express the volume dependence of the entropy in the form of the expansion

$$\Delta S = S(T, V) - S(T, V_0) = \left(\frac{\beta}{\chi_T}\right)_V \Delta V\left(1 - \frac{X}{2}\frac{\Delta V}{V_0} + \cdots\right) \quad (6.16)$$

Continuing with the collection of equations which will be employed later in evaluating the explicit anharmonic contributions to the heat capacity and entropy, we may record the equation

$$\Delta C_V^{\mathrm{anh}}(V_T)/\Delta C_V^{\mathrm{anh}}(V_0) = (V/V_0)^{\gamma^{\mathrm{anh}}} \quad (6.17)$$

in which γ^{anh} may be written as $\{\partial [\ln A(V)]/\partial (\ln V)\}_T$, $A(V)$ being part of the first-order coefficient in the expansion for the anharmonic contribution to the heat capacity and entropy, defined in Eq. (6.1).

For values of $T \geq \theta^C$ we may write

$$[\gamma(T, V_0) - \gamma^{\mathrm{qh}}(T, V_0)] = [\gamma^{\mathrm{anh}} - \gamma^{\mathrm{qh}}(T, V_0)] \, \varDelta C_V^{\mathrm{anh}}(T, V_0) \qquad (6.18)$$

which will be used later to obtain a first approximation to γ^{anh} and hence a first approximation to $\varDelta C_V^{\mathrm{anh}}(V_0)$, using a reiterative procedure. Rewriting Eq. (6.8) in the form

$$\gamma^{\mathrm{qh}}(V_0) = [\gamma(V_0)C_V(V_0) - \gamma^{\mathrm{anh}} \, \varDelta C_V^{\mathrm{anh}}(V_0)]/C_V^{\mathrm{qh}}(V_0)$$
$$\approx \gamma_\infty^{\mathrm{qh}}(V_0) \qquad \text{when} \qquad T \geq \theta^C \qquad (6.19)$$

gives a value of $\gamma_\infty^{\mathrm{qh}}(V_0)$ which is required in Eq. (6.13) to give $S^{\mathrm{qh}}(V)$. In this application of Eq. (6.19), $C_V(V)$ may be used for $C_V(V_0)$ with negligible error.

6.5. ANALYTICAL PROCEDURE

We have now assembled equations necessary for a quantitative analytical examination of the occurrence of explicit anharmonic contributions to the thermal properties of a solid. Having expressed experimentally determined data for the heat capacity, thermal expansion, elastic constants, and the pressure variation of the bulk modulus in the appropriate forms using thermodynamic relationships, we may first derive the quantities Y and X defined in Eqs. (6.12) and (6.14). These may be checked for consistency with the aid of Eq. (6.15). The value of the Grüneisen parameter $\gamma = \beta V/C_P \chi_S$ may then be corrected to the volume at $T = 0$ with the aid of Y substituted in Eq. (6.11). Using the Euler transformation described earlier, the variable in Eq. (6.10) may be transformed from T to $t = [1 + (T/0.2\theta_\infty^C)^2]^{-1}$. Substituting the values of $\gamma(T, V_0)$ obtained by correction above then allows the determination of $\gamma_\infty^{\mathrm{qh}}(V_0)$ by the extrapolation of the transformed equation (6.10) to $t = 0$.

As a next step we may employ the procedure described in Chapter 5 to determine the values of the Debye temperatures corresponding to the quasiharmonic specific heat by extrapolation of a graph of $[\theta(T, V)]^2$ against T^{-2} from the approximate temperature region $\theta_\infty^C/6 < T < \theta_\infty^C/3$ to $T^{-2} = 0$. The value of the intercept gives $\theta^{\mathrm{qh}}(\infty, V)$, and the various values of $\theta^{\mathrm{qh}}(T, V)$ corresponding to the evaluation lead to corresponding values of $C_V^{\mathrm{qh}}(T, V)$. Subtracting these values of $C_V^{\mathrm{qh}}(T, V)$ from the values of C_V

corresponding to the experimentally determined C_P, i.e., $C_V^{ex}(T, V)$, gives the anharmonic contribution to the heat capacity $\Delta C_V^{anh}(T, V)$. Leading to the volume correction of this quantity, it is possible next to estimate the anharmonic contribution to the Grüneisen parameter γ^{anh}, defined in Eq. (6.8), with the aid of Eq. (6.18), employing a reiterative procedure as follows. Equation (6.18) is of the form $z = xy$, in which $y = \Delta C_V^{anh}(T, V_0)$. A first approximation to γ^{anh} may therefore be obtained by plotting a graph of z against y, in which values of $\Delta C_V^{anh}(T, V)$ just derived may be used for y in the absence of a knowledge of $\Delta C_V^{anh}(T, V_0)$. Substituting the value of γ^{anh} so obtained in Eq. (6.17) leads to a first estimate of $\Delta C_V^{anh}(T, V_0)$, which may be substituted in Eq. (6.18) to give a better estimate of γ^{anh}. Reiterating in this fashion leads to constant values of γ^{anh} and $\Delta C_V^{anh}(T, V_0)$. These values may be substituted in Eq. (6.19) to yield $\gamma_\infty^{qh}(V_0)$. The consistency of $\gamma_\infty^{qh}(V_0)$ and γ^{anh} may be checked at this point.

A first approximation to the first anharmonic coefficient which appeared in Eqs. (6.5)–(6.7) may be determined in a form corresponding to the fixed volume characteristic of $T = 0$, through Eq. (6.7) by using the value of $\Delta C_V^{anh}(T, V_0)$ determined above, and neglecting terms in the second and higher powers of T. In order to provide an independent determination of $A(V_0)$ we require to know the anharmonic contribution to the entropy. In order to estimate this we may begin by determining the Debye temperature corresponding to the entropy, correcting the values to the constant volume V_0 corresponding to $T = 0$ using Eq. (5.34), extrapolating a plot of $[\theta^S(T, V_0)]^2$ versus T^{-2} to $T = \infty$ to give $\theta_\infty^S(\infty, V_0)$, and correcting this approximately for constant-volume anharmonicity using the value of $A(V_0)$ determined above. $\theta_{qh}^S(\infty, V)$ may then be calculated to a good approximation from Eq. (6.13) using the value of $\gamma_\infty^{qh}(V_0)$ determined above, and using Y in place of Y'. At this stage sufficient derivations will have been performed to permit the evaluation of

$$\Delta S^{anh}(V_0) = S^{ex}(V_0) - S^{qh}(V_0)$$

from which an alternative first estimate of $A(V_0)$ may be deduced with the aid of Eq. (6.6), neglecting terms in the second and higher powers of T. Comparison with the value of $A(V_0)$ derived from the specific heats provides a useful check on the self-consistency of the analytical scheme, though a precise value of $A(V_0)$ based upon an entropy determination calls for a high degree of precision in the heat capacity values over a wider temperature range than is necessary for a determination based upon specific heats.

With the aid of particularly precise experimental data it is possible to carry the analysis a stage further, and to estimate the second-order anharmonic coefficient $B(V)$ which appears in Eqs. (6.5)–(6.7). For example, this may be obtained from the slope of a graph of $[\Delta S^{\mathrm{anh}}(T, V)]/T$ or $[\Delta C^{\mathrm{anh}}(T, V)]/T$ against T, neglecting the third-order coefficient. If the precision of the experimental data is abnormally high, an attempt may be made to estimate the third-order coefficient $C(V)$.

Leadbetter (1968c) has drawn attention to one difficulty in the foregoing procedure, and that concerns the pressure (or volume) variations of the isothermal and adiabatic bulk moduli, knowledge of which is required in order to evaluate Y and X. Such quantities are not usually known at the temperatures at which anharmonic effects are most serious, and it becomes necessary to make some assumption concerning their temperature dependence. In fact, Leadbetter assumed temperature independence of these volume dependences, and in assessing the influence of this assumption he concluded that the effect on the entropy was probably small but that the influence on the heat capacity was difficult to assess. The determination of $\Delta C_V^{\mathrm{anh}}(T, V)$ itself, on the other hand, does not involve Y or X at all, though the calculated volume dependence of $\Delta C_V^{\mathrm{anh}}$ will not be known very accurately because of uncertainties in γ^{anh}.

6.6. ANHARMONIC FREQUENCY SHIFTS

Barron (1964) showed that it was possible to represent the influence of anharmonicity upon atomic vibrations in terms of shifts in the vibrational frequencies which are respectively purely volume-dependent and purely temperature-dependent. Thus for an individual vibrational frequency $v_j(T, V)$ we may write

$$v_j(T, V) = v_j^{\mathrm{qh}}(V) + \Delta v_j(T, V)$$
$$= v_j^{\mathrm{qh}}(V)\{1 + [\Delta v_j(T, V)/v_j^{\mathrm{qh}}(V)]\}$$

In this expression Δv_j is the explicitly temperature-dependent anharmonic shift, and the purely volume-dependent shift is incorporated in $v_j^{\mathrm{qh}}(V)$. From purely thermodynamic measurements it is not possible to study the behavior of the individual modes. However, we may examine the influence of volume and temperature separately on averages of the frequencies, expressed in terms of the moments. Thus we may write the volume change in the maximum frequency of the Debye distribution having the same nth moment as the spectrum in the actual crystal to the first order as

$$\Delta v_{\mathrm{D}}(n)/v_{\mathrm{D}}(n) = -\gamma(n)(\Delta V)/V_0 \qquad (6.20)$$

Similarly, the temperature dependence may be expressed as

$$\{\partial [\ln \nu_D(n)]/\partial T\}_P = -\beta \gamma(n) \tag{6.21}$$

Turning to functions which are experimentally more amenable, Leadbetter (1968c) has shown that the entropy at high temperatures may be written in the form

$$S(T, V) = 3 \mathcal{N} k \left\{ 1 - \ln \frac{h \nu_g^{qh}(V)}{kT} \left[1 + \frac{\Delta \nu_g(T, V)}{\nu_g^{qh}} \right] + O(T^{-2}) \right\} \tag{6.22}$$

to the first order in $\Delta \nu / \nu$ (see Salter, 1955), in which

$$\Delta S^{anh}(T, V)/3 \mathcal{N} k = -\Delta \nu_g/\nu_g$$

The corresponding equation for the heat capacity is

$$C_V(T, V) = 3 \mathcal{N} k \left\{ 1 - \left[\frac{d(\Delta \nu_g/\nu_g)}{d(\ln T)} \right]_V \right\}$$

and

$$\frac{\Delta C_V^{anh}(T, V)}{3 \mathcal{N} k} = - \left[\frac{\partial(\ln \nu_g)}{\partial(\ln T)} \right]_V = - \left[\frac{\partial(\Delta \nu_g/\nu_g)}{\partial(\ln T)} \right]_V \tag{6.23}$$

From Eqs. (6.6) and (6.7), to the first order in T we may write

$$\Delta S^{anh}/3 \mathcal{N} k = \Delta C_V^{anh}/3 \mathcal{N} k = A(V)T \tag{6.24}$$

Equating the right-hand sides of Eqs. (6.23) and (6.24) and integrating gives the result

$$\Delta \nu_g/\nu_g = -A(V)T \tag{6.25}$$

This explicit temperature-dependent constant-volume shift in the geometric mean frequency ν_g may be combined with the shift due to volume change, given by Eq. (6.20), after putting $n = 0$, to give a total shift which may be compared with values estimated from infrared absorption and Raman and neutron scattering experiments.

The combined effect of the calculated volume and temperature contributions to the shifts produced in the maximum frequencies of the equivalent Debye distributions corresponding to $n = -2$ and -3 in the negative moments may also be derived from experimental results. In particular the total shift in $\nu_D(-3)$, which is directly related to the low-temperature limiting value of the Debye characteristic temperature, may be derived from the measured elastic constants, and that in $\nu_D(-2)$ may be obtained from Debye–Waller measurements.

Barron *et al.* (1963) have shown how the purely volume-dependent contribution to the Debye–Waller factor θ^M might be derived from thermodynamic data for copper, which correlated well with X-ray measurements. Salter (1965) extended applications of this kind to germanium and silicon, employing Padé approximants in regions between those appropriate to high- and low-temperature limits. Yates (1966) did likewise with potassium bromide and magnesium oxide, and Brade and Yates (1969) made favorable comparisons of calculations of this type with experimental neutron scattering results for alkaline earth fluorides. For the present purpose it will suffice to look at the general principles involved and to note the results for the limiting cases of low and high temperatures. In principle, the image of X- or similar radiation diffracted by a crystal would be expected to become more diffuse as the amplitude of vibrations of the atoms increased with temperature. The intensity I of a Bragg reflection from a crystal at a finite temperature may be related to the corresponding intensity from the static lattice I_0 by the equation

$$I = I_0 \exp[-2M(T)]$$

where $M(T)$ is the Debye–Waller factor, which in turn is related to the atomic amplitudes of vibration by

$$M(T) = (8\pi^2 \overline{u^2} \sin^2\theta)/\lambda^2$$

In this equation $\overline{u^2}$ is the mean-squared displacement of an atom perpendicular to the diffracting plane, θ is the Bragg angle, and λ is the wavelength of the incident radiation. It is convenient next to express $\overline{u^2}$ in terms of a temperature factor $B(T)$ in the form

$$B(T) = 8\pi\overline{u^2}$$

Benson and Gill (1966) have expressed $B(T)$ in the form

$$W(x) = mkT/6h^2 B(T)$$

where

$$W(x) = \frac{3\hbar^2}{kTx^2}\left(\frac{x}{4} + \frac{1}{x}\int_0^x \frac{y}{e^y - 1}\, dy\right)$$

in which $x = h\nu_m/kT = \theta/T$ and $y = h\nu/kT$. In order to facilitate calculations involving these quantities they have evaluated the above integral and tabulated the results. Barron *et al.* (1963) expressed $W(x)$ in the form of series expansions appropriate to low and high temperatures. In particular,

$$\theta_0^M = (h/k)\nu_D(-1) \quad \text{and} \quad \theta_\infty^M = (h/k)\nu_D(-2)$$

at the two limits, as was mentioned in Eqs. (5.22) and (5.23), and series expansions may be written:

$$\theta^M(T) = \theta_0^M \{1 + 6.580[1 - (\theta_0^M/\theta_0^C)^3](T/\theta_0^M)^2 \cdots \}$$

at low temperatures, and

$$\theta^M(T) = \theta_\infty^M \big(1 + (1/7,200)[(\theta_\infty^C/\theta_\infty^M)^2 - 1](\theta_\infty^M/T)^4$$
$$+ (1/423,360)\{1 - [\nu_D(4)/\nu_D(-2)]^4\}(\theta_\infty^M/T)^6 + \cdots \big)$$

at high temperatures. A comprehensive description of the physical significance of Debye–Waller factors has been given by Barron et al. (1966). In investigating anharmonicity we are principally interested in high-temperature effects, and from a knowledge of the measured variation of θ^M with temperature at high temperatures we may gain a measure of the sum of the effects of volume dependence and explicit temperature dependence of the vibrations. Measurements of heat capacity, thermal expansion, and elastic constants at much lower temperatures provide the means of estimating the purely volume-dependent contribution to the variation of θ^M, through Eq. (6.20), and subtracting the frequency shift resulting from the single effect from the result corresponding to the combined effect yields the explicitly temperature-dependent shift in $\nu_D(-2)$.

Barron (1964) pointed out that at $T \sim 0.3\theta_\infty^C$ the thermal energy E_T of a solid is only approximately one-third of the zero-point energy E_Z, and the mean amplitude of vibration is not much greater than at $T = 0$. He concluded that since a sharp onset of anharmonicity was inconceivable, appreciable anharmonicity must be present down to the lowest temperatures. At $T = 0$ frequency shifts arising from the energy of zero-point vibrations will exist, and Leadbetter (1968c) has shown how these may be estimated. He applied the foregoing analytical scheme to experimental high-temperature thermodynamic data for lead and aluminum. In the case of lead he concluded that there was no need to suppose the occurrence of vacancy formation in order to explain the observations. In the cases of both lead and aluminum he found that the coefficient A in the leading term in the expansion for the anharmonic contribution to the free energy, entropy, and specific heat was negative, in agreement with a conclusion based upon earlier theoretical models for close-packed crystals due to Leibfried and Ludwig (1961),

Maradudin *et al.* (1961), and Wallace (1965). Concluding an excellent development of his analytical scheme, Leadbetter observed that the total anharmonic shifts in the geometric mean frequency with temperature, calculated from the volume dependence determined through the quasi-harmonic contribution to the Grüneisen parameter and the explicit temperature dependence determined through the analysis of the specific heat, were in excellent agreement with the frequency shifts given by experimental inelastic neutron scattering experiments for both lead and aluminum. In a later paper, Leadbetter *et al.* (1969) have extended analyses of this kind to sodium chloride, potassium chloride, and potassium bromide. The calculations are satisfactorily self-consistent and in the case of potassium bromide the calculated total temperature dependence of the geometric mean frequency agrees very well with that based upon inelastic neutron scattering experiments. The authors concluded that experimentally observed anharmonic quantities provided the means of applying a particularly stringent test for calculations on atomic models.

After examining the heat capacity measurements of Flubacher *et al.* (1959a) on germanium and silicon, Newsham (1966) concluded that the rapid fall in the Debye characteristic temperature accompanying increasing temperature above approximately $\theta^C_\infty/3$ could not reasonably be accounted for in terms of errors in $C_P - C_V$ corrections or vacancy formation. He proceeded to calculate the coefficients in the leading terms of the anharmonic components of the heat capacities, which turned out to be approximately double the corresponding values for typical alkali halides. Supporting his belief in the origin of the curvature lying in anharmonic effects, he observed further that the first anharmonic coefficient for silicon was approximately 27% greater than that of germanium, which was in keeping with the fact that the ratio of the amplitude of vibration to the interatomic spacing was approximately 30% greater in silicon than in germanium at 300°K. Analyzing their measurements of the thermal expansivities of sodium chloride and potassium chloride up to temperatures exceeding 900°C, Leadbetter and Newsham (1969) observed increasingly marked curvatures in the graphs connecting the thermal expansion coefficients with temperature. Assuming that this behavior arose from vacancy formation, they calculated the corresponding vacancy concentrations and compared the figures derived with those based upon the analysis of conductivity data. In the case of potassium chloride the figure based upon the thermal expansion measurements worked out to be too high by a factor of 50. In the case of sodium chloride the corresponding discrepancy factor was 15. It was concluded that the assumed cause of the curvature in the thermal expansion graphs was incorrect, and that the true origin was to be found in higher-order anharmonic effects than those considered so far. Leadbetter and Settatree (1969) observed curvature in graphs connecting the specific heats of sodium chloride, potassium chloride, and potassium bromide with temperature up to 500°C. Pursuing the same general idea as that described in connection with the thermal expansion measurements, the authors compared the result of attempting to account for the curvature in terms of vacancy formation with calculations of vacancy concentration based upon ionic conductivity data. Again the values based upon the thermodynamic data were very much higher than those based upon the conductivity. Since the latter are well established it was again concluded that an explanation of the results was more likely to be found in higher-order anharmonic effects than those considered here. In spite of any apparent evidence for defect formation, arising from agreement between deductions based upon thermal expansion and specific heat data, the conclusion that extreme care should be exercised in attempts to derive information about this phenomenon from thermal properties is extremely important.

Appendix

Except where it is explicitly stated to the contrary, the following definitions refer to the more important symbols used in the text.

$a, b, c, \ldots$	constants and/or integers
a, a_1, a_2	amplitudes of vibration
c_{ij}	"elastic stiffness constants" or "moduli of elasticity"
c_l	velocity of longitudinal vibrations
c_t	velocity of transverse vibrations
C_e	electronic contribution to the specific heat
C_{har}	the "harmonic" specific heat
C_P	specific heat at constant pressure
C_V	specific heat at constant volume
e	electronic charge
E	energy
E_T	thermal energy
E_Z	zero-point energy
$f(\varepsilon)$	Fermi distribution function
$f(\nu)$	number of normal modes of vibration of frequency ν per unit frequency range
$F, F(T, V)$	Helmholtz free energy
$F(\varepsilon_0)$	density of electron energy states at the Fermi surface
g	electron spin weighting factor
h	Planck's constant
k	Boltzmann's constant
$\mathbf{k}$	reduced momentum
K	bulk modulus of elasticity
K_S	adiabatic bulk modulus of elasticity
K_T	isothermal bulk modulus of elasticity
m	mass

n	modulus of rigidity
N	Avogadro's number
$\mathcal{N}$	number of vibrating particles in an assembly
$\mathbf{p}$	momentum
P	pressure
R	gas constant
s_{ij}	"elastic compliance constants" or "elastic constants"
S	entropy
$\mathcal{S}$	surface area
T	absolute temperature
$\overline{u^2}$	mean-square amplitude of vibration
U	internal energy
$\bar{U}$	mean energy of oscillation of a gram atom
V	volume
$V(r)$	potential
Y	Young's modulus of elasticity
β	volume coefficient of thermal expansion
γ	Grüneisen parameter
γ_e	electronic heat coefficient
γ_0	low-temperature limiting value of the Grüneisen parameter
γ_∞	high-temperature limiting value of the Grüneisen parameter
ε	electron energy
ε_0	maximum electron energy in the completely degenerate state
θ	Bragg angle
θ_E	the Einstein temperature
θ_F	the Fermi temperature
θ_{har}	the Debye temperature corresponding to the "harmonic" specific heat
θ_N	the characteristic temperature corresponding to the theory of Nernst and Lindemann
θ_0	low-temperature limiting value of the Debye characteristic temperature
θ_∞	high-temperature limiting value of the Debye characteristic temperature
θ^C	Debye characteristic temperature corresponding to specific heat
θ^{el}	the Debye characteristic temperature corresponding to elasticity measurements
θ_0^M	low-temperature limiting value of the Debye–Waller factor
θ_∞^M	high-temperature limiting value of the Debye–Waller factor
λ	wavelength

ν	frequency
ν_{D}	cutoff frequency of the Debye distribution
$\nu_{\mathrm{D}}(n)$	maximum frequency of the Debye distribution having the same nth moment as the vibrational spectrum in the actual crystal
ν_{E}	the Einstein frequency
$\nu(\varepsilon)\,d\varepsilon$	number of electron energy states in the energy range $d\varepsilon$
ν_g	geometric mean frequency of the vibrational frequency spectrum
ν_l	cutoff frequency of longitudinal lattice vibrations in the theory of Born and von Kármán
$\overline{\nu^n}$	nth moment of frequency ν
ν_t	cutoff frequency of transverse lattice vibrations in the theory of Born and von Kármán
σ	Poissons's ratio
ϕ	potential energy
χ_S	adiabatic compressibility
χ_T	isothermal compressibility

Subscripts or superscripts

anh	anharmonic
ex	experimental
qh	quasiharmonic

References

Adachi, K., Suga, H., and Seki, S., 1968, *Bull. Chem. Soc. Japan* **41**, 1073.

Andres, K., 1961, *Cryogenics* **2**, 93.

Bailey, A. C., and Yates, B., 1967*a*, *Phil. Mag.* **16**, 1241.

Bailey, A. C., and Yates, B., 1967*b*, *Proc. Phys. Soc.* **91**, 390.

Bailey, A. C., and Yates, B., 1969, UKAEA TRG Report 1874 (C/X).

Bailey, A. C., Waterhouse, N., and Yates, B., 1969, *J. Phys. C* (*Solid State Phys.*) **2**, 769.

Barker, R. E., 1967, *J. Appl. Phys.* **38**, 4234.

Barron, T. H. K., 1955, *Phil. Mag.* **46**, 720.

Barron, T. H. K., 1957, *Ann. Phys. N. Y.* **1**, 77.

Barron, T. H. K., 1964, Proc. Int. Conf. on Lattice Dynamics, Copenaghen, 1963 (London: Pergamon Press), p. 247.

Barron, T. H. K., and Klein, M. L., 1962, *Phys. Rev.* **127**, 1997.

Barron, T. H. K., and Morrison, J. A., 1960, *Proc. Roy. Soc.* **A256**, 427.

Barron, T. H. K., and Munn, R. W., 1967, *Phil. Mag.* **15**, 85.

Barron, T. H. K., Berg, W. T., and Morrison, J. A., 1957, *Proc. Roy. Soc.* **A242**, 478.

Barron, T. H. K., Leadbetter, A. J., Morrison, J. A., and Salter, L. S., 1963, Inelastic Scattering of Neutrons in Solids and Liquids (Vienna: International Atomic Energy Agency), Vol. 1, p. 49.

Barron, T. H. K., Leadbetter, A. J., and Morrison, J. A., 1964, *Proc. Roy. Soc.* **A279**, 62.

Barron, T. H. K., Leadbetter, A. J., Morrison, J. A., and Salter, L. S., 1966, *Acta Cryst.* **20**, 125.

Bartels, R. A., and Schuele, D. E., 1965, *J. Phys. Chem. Solids* **26**, 537.

Batchelder, D. N., and Simmons, R. O., 1965, *J. Appl. Phys.* **36**, 2864.

Belhami, O., Merck, M., Perréard, E., Peter, M., and Walker, E., 1966, *Helv. Phys. Acta* **39**, 338.

Bell, R. J., Bird, N. F., and Dean, P., 1968, *J. Phys. C* (*Proc. Phys. Soc.*) **1**, 299.

Benson, G. C., and Gill, E. K., 1966, *Can. J. Phys.* **44**, 674.

Berg, W. T., and Morrison, J. A., 1957, *Proc. Roy. Soc.* **A242**, 467.

Bijl, D., and Pullan, H., 1955, *Physica* **21**, 285.

Blackman, M., 1935*a*, *Proc. Roy. Soc.* **148A**, 365.

Blackman, M., 1935*b*, *Proc. Roy. Soc.* **149A**, 117.

Blackman, M., 1937*a*, *Proc. Roy. Soc.* **159A**, 416.

Blackman, M., 1937*b*, *Proc. Camb. Phil. Soc.* **33**, 94.

Blackman, M., 1955, *in* Handbuch der Physik, Vol. 7, p. 325.

Blackman, M., 1956, *Acta Cryst.* **9**, 734.

Blackman, M., 1958, *Phil. Mag.* **3**, 831.

Born, M., and von Kármán, T., 1912, *Phys. Z.* **13**, 297.

Born, M., and von Kármán, T., 1913, *Phys. Z.* **14**, 15, 65.

Brade, R. M., and Yates, B., 1969, *Phys. Stat. Sol.* **36**, 551.

Bridgman, P. W., 1928, *Z. Krist.* **67**, 363.

Buckingham, M. J., and Schafroth, M. R., 1954, *Proc. Phys. Soc.* **A67**, 828.

Budworth, D. W., Hoare, F. E., and Preston, J., 1960, *Proc. Roy. Soc.* **A257**, 250.

Buffington, R. M., and Latimer, W. M., 1926, *J. Am. Chem. Soc.* **48**, 2305.

Bunton, G. V., and Weintroub, S., 1968, *Cryogenics* **8**, 354.

Bunton, G. V., and Weintroub, S., 1969, *J. Phys. C (Solid State Phys.)*, **2**, 116.

Carr, R. H., and Swenson, C. A., 1964, *Cryogenics* **4**, 76.

Carr, R. H., McCammon, R. D., and White, G. K., 1964, *Proc. Roy. Soc.* **A280**, 72.

Chambers, R. G., 1961, *Proc. Phys. Soc.* **78**, 941.

Chang, S. S., Horman, J. A., and Bestul, A. B., 1967, *J. Res. Nat. Bur. Std.* **71A**, 293.

Chang, Z. P., Barsch, G. R., and Miller, D. L., 1967, *Phys. Stat. Sol.* **23**, 577.

Channing, D. A., and Weintroub, S., 1965, *Can. J. Phys.* **43**, 1328.

Clark, A. E., and Strakna, R. E., 1962, *Phys. Chem. Glasses* **3**, 121.

Clusius, K., Goldmann, J., and Perlick, A., 1949, *Z. Naturforsch* **4a**, 424.

Collins, J. G., Cowan, J. A., and White, G. K., 1967, *Cryogenics* **7**, 219.

Corviovei, A., and Motoc, C., 1963, *Acta Physica Academiae Scientiarum Hungaricae* **15**, 299.

Daniels, W. B., and Smith, C. S., 1958, *Phys. Rev.* **111**, 713.

Dauphinee, T. M., and Woods, S. B., 1955, *Rev. Sci. Instr.* **26**, 693.

Debye, P., 1912, *Ann. Phys. Lpz.* **39**, 789.

Debye, P., 1913, *Phys. Z.* **14**, 259.

Dixon, M., Hoare, F. E., and Holden, T. M., 1967, *Proc. Phys. Soc.* **90**, 253.

Domb, C. and Salter, L., 1952, *Phil. Mag.* **43**, 1083.

Donaldson, R. H., and Lanchester, P. C., 1968, *J. Phys. C (Proc. Phys. Soc.)* **1**, 364.

Dugdale, J. S., Morrison, J. A., and Patterson, D., 1954, *Proc. Roy. Soc.* **A224**, 228.

Dupuis, M., Mazo, R., and Onsager, L., 1960, *J. Chem. Phys.* **33**, 1452.

Edmonds, D. T., and Petersen, R. G., 1959, *Phys. Rev. Lett.* **1**, 499.

Einstein, A., 1907, *Ann. Phys.* **22**, 180.

Feldman, J. L., 1964, *Proc. Phys. Soc.* **84**, 361.

Figgins, B. F., Jones, G. O., and Riley, D. P., 1956, *Phil. Mag.* **1**, 747.

Fine, P. C., 1939, *Verh. Dtsch. Phys. Ges.* **15**, 571.

Fizeau, H., 1864, *Ann. Chim. Phys.* **2**.

Fizeau, H., 1866, *Ann. Chim. Phys.* **8**, 335.

Flubacher, P., Leadbetter, A. J., and Morrison, J. A. 1959a, *Phil. Mag.* **4**, 273.

Flubacher, P., Leadbetter, A. J., Morrison, J. A., and Stoicheff, B. P., 1959b, *J. Phys. Chem. Solids* **12**, 53.

Flubacher, P., Leadbetter, A. J., and Morrison, J. A., 1960a, *J. Chem. Phys.* **33**, 1751.

Flubacher, P., Leadbetter, A. J., and Morrison, J. A., 1960b, *J. Phys. Chem. Solids* **13**, 160.

Forgacs, R. L., 1958, *Proc. Nat. Electronics Conf.* **14**, 528.

Fritz, J. J., Davies, R. L., Bernard, H. W., and Aston, J. G., 1967, *J. Chem. Phys.* **47**, 3693.

Ganesan, S., and Srinivasan, R., 1963, *Proc. Roy. Soc.* **A271**, 154.

Gerlich, D., 1964a, *Phys. Rev.* **135**, A1331.

Gerlich, D., 1964b, *Phys. Rev.* **136**, A1366.

Giauque, W. F., Geballe, T. H., Lyon, D. N., and Fritz, J. J., 1952, *Rev. Sci. Instr.* **23**, 169.

Gluyas, M., Hughes, F. D., and James, B. W., 1970, *J. Phys. E.* **3**, 132.

Goodenough, J. B., 1966, Magnetism and the Chemical Bond (London: Interscience).

Gopal, E. S. R., 1966, Specific Heats at Low Temperatures (London: Heywood).

Gotlib, Yu. Ya., and Sochava, I. V., 1963, *Soviet Phys.—Doklady* **7**, 1024.

Grüneisen, E., 1926, *in* Handbuch der Physik (Berlin: Springer), Vol. 10, p. 1.

Guseinov, N. G., and Seidov, Yu. M., 1966, *Soviet Phys.—Solid State* **7**, 2929.

Hirschkoff, E. C., and Wolcott, N. M., 1965, *Proc. Phys. Soc.* **86**, 1372.

Ho, P. S., and Ruoff, A. L., 1967, *Phys. Rev.* **161**, 864.

Hoare, F. E., and Yates, B., 1957, *Proc. Roy. Soc.* **A240**, 42.

Huffman, D. R., and Norwood, M. H., 1960, *Phys. Rev.* **117**, 709.

Hughes, T. J., and Brittain, J. O., 1964, *Phys. Rev.* **135**, A1738.

Huntington, H. B., 1958, *in* Solid State Physics (New York: Academic Press), Vol. 7, p. 213.

Huzan, E., Abbiss, C. P., and Jones, G. O., 1961, *Phil. Mag.* **6**, 277.

Hwang, J. L., 1954, *J. Chem. Phys.* **22**, 154.

James, B. W., and Yates, B., 1963, *J. Sci. Instr.* **40**, 193.

James, B. W., and Yates, B., 1965, *Cryogenics* **5**, 68.

Jones, R. V., 1961, *J. Sci. Instr.* **38**, 37.

Karo, A. M., 1959, *J. Chem. Phys.* **31**, 1489.

Karo, A. M., 1960, *J. Chem. Phys.* **33**, 7.

Katz, E., 1951, *J. Chem. Phys.* **19**, 488.

Keeler, G. J., 1969, Thesis, London University.

Kellermann, E. W., 1941, *Proc. Roy. Soc.* **A178**, 17.

Kerner, E. H., 1956, *Proc. Phys. Soc.* **B69**, 808.

Kirby, R. K., 1956, *J. Res. Nat. Bur. Std.* **57**, 91.

Kirkham, A. J., and Yates. B., 1968, *J. Phys. C* (*Proc. Phys. Soc.*) **1**, 1162.

Kittel, C., 1957, Introduction to Solid State Physics (London: Wiley).

Laquer, H. L., and Head, E. L., 1952, AECU-2161, U. S. Atomic Energy Commission.

de Launay, J., 1954, *J. Chem. Phys.* **22**, 1676.

de Launay, J., 1956a, *J. Chem. Phys.* **24**, 1071.

de Launay, J., 1956b, *Solid State Phys.* **2**, 219.

de Launay, J., 1959, *J. Chem. Phys.* **30**, 91.

Lazarus, D., 1949, *Phys. Rev.* **76**, 545.

Leadbetter, A. J., 1965, *Proc. Roy. Soc.* **A287**, 403.

Leadbetter, A. J., 1968a, *Phys. Chem. Glasses* **9**, 1.

Leadbetter, A. J., 1968b, *J. Phys. C* (*Proc. Phys. Soc.*) **1**, 1481.

Leadbetter, A. J., 1968c, *J. Phys. C* (*Proc. Phys. Soc.*) **1**, 1489.

Leadbetter, A. J., and Morrison, J. A., 1963, *Phys. Chem. Glasses* **4**, 188.

Leadbetter, A. J., and Newsham, D. M. T., 1969, *J. Phys. C* (*Solid State Phys.*) **2**, 210.

Leadbetter, A. J., and Settatree, G. R., 1969, *J. Phys. C* (*Solid State Phys.*) **2**, 385.

Leadbetter, A. J., Newsham, D. M. T., and Settatree, G. R., 1969, *J. Phys. C* (*Solid State Phys.*) **2**, 393.

Leibfried, G., and Ludwig, W., 1961, *in* Solid State Physics (New York: Academic Press), Vol. 12, p. 275.

Leighton, R. B., 1948, *Rev. Mod. Phys.* **20**, 165.

Lewis, J. T., Lehoczky, A., and Briscoe, C. V., 1967, *Phys. Rev.* **161**, 877.

Lord, A. E., 1967, *J. Phys. Chem. Solids* **28**, 517.

Lyon, W. G., and Westrum, E. F., 1968, *J. Chem. Phys.* **49**, 3374.

Maradudin, A. A., and Wallis, R. F., 1966, *Phys. Rev.* **148**, 945.

Maradudin, A. A., Flinn, P. A., and Coldwell-Horsfall, R. A., 1961, *Ann. Phys., N.Y.* **15**, 360.

Marshall, B. J., and Miller, R. E., 1967, *J. Appl. Phys.* **38**, 4749.

Marshall, B. J., Pederson, D. O., and Dorris, G. G., 1967, *J. Phys. Chem. Solids* **28**, 1061.

Matsuo, T., Suga, H., and Seki, S., 1968, *Bull. Chem. Soc. Japan* **41**, 583.

McCammon, R. D., and White, G. K., 1965, *Phil. Mag.* **22**, 1125.

McSkimin, H. J., and Andreatch, P., 1963, *J. Appl. Phys.* **34**, 651.

Meincke, P. P. M., and Graham, G. M., 1963, *in* Proc. 8th. Int. Conf. on Low-Temperature Physics (London: Butterworth), p. 399.

Meincke, P. P. M., and Graham, G. M., 1965, *Can. J. Phys.* **43**, 1853.

Merritt, G. E., 1933, *J. Res. Nat. Bur. Std.* **10**, 59.

Meyerhoff, R. W., and Smith, J. F., 1962, *J. Appl. Phys.* **33**, 219.

Montroll, E., 1950, *J. Chem. Phys.* **18**, 183.

Morrison, J. A., and Patterson, D., 1956. *Trans. Faraday Soc.* **52**, 764.

Morse, G. E., and Lawson, A. W., 1967, *J. Phys. Chem. Solids* **28**, 939.

Nagamiya, T., Yosida, K., and Kubo, R., 1955, *Advan. Phys.* **4**, 1.

Nernst, W., and Lindemann, F. A., 1911, *Z. Elektrochem.* **17**, 817.

Newsham, D. M. T., 1966, *Phys. Rev.* **152**, 841.

Nikanorov, S. P., and Stepanov, A. V., 1965, *Soviet Phys.—Solid State* **6**, 1569.

Nikanorov, S. P., Nran'yan, A. A., and Stepanov, A. V., 1965, *Soviet Phys.—Solid State* **6**, 1576.

Nix, F. C., and MacNair, D., 1941, *Rev. Sci. Instr.* **12**, 66.

Overton, W. C., 1962, *J. Chem. Phys.* **37**, 2975.

Overton, W. C., 1966, *J. Chem. Phys.* **44**, 934.

Parkinson, D. H., 1958, *Rep. Prog. Phys.* **21**, 226.

Parkinson, D. H., and Quarrington, J. E., 1954, *Proc. Phys. Soc.* **A67**, 569.

Perez-Albuerne, E. A., and Drickamer, H. G., 1965, *J. Chem. Phys.* **43**, 1381.

Pojur, A. F., and Yates, B., 1968, *J. Sci. Instr.* (*J. Phys. E*) **1**, 948.

Reese, W., Higgins, P. J., and Rostine, G. W., 1968, *J. Appl. Phys.* **39**, 1800.

Reinitz, K., 1961, *Phys. Rev.* **213**, 1615.

Rose-Innes, A. C., 1964, Low-Temperature Techniques: The Use of Liquid Helium in the Laboratory (London: E. U. P.).

Rubin, T., Altman, H. W., and Johnston, H. L., 1954, *J. Am. Chem. Soc.* **76**, 5289.

Salter, L., 1955, *Proc. Roy. Soc.* **A233**, 418.

Salter, L. S., 1965, *Advan. Phys.* **14**, 1.

Schottky, W., 1922, *Phys. Z.* **23**, 448.

Scott, J. F., 1968, *J. Chem. Phys.* **48**, 874.

Settatree, G. R., 1968, Thesis, Bristol University.

Shapiro, J. M., Taylor, D. R., and Graham, G. M., 1964, *Can. J. Phys.* **42**, 835.

Sheard, F. W., 1958, *Phil. Mag.* **3**, 1381.

Sherman, J., 1932, *Chem. Revs.* **11**, 93.

Simmons, R. O., and Balluffi, R. W., 1964, *J. Phys. Chem. Solids* **25**, 1139.

Smith, H. J., 1947, *Phil. Trans.* **A188**, 179.

Sorai, M., 1967, Thesis, Osaka University.

Sorai, M., 1968, *J. Phys. Soc. Japan.* **25**, 421.

Srinivasan, R., 1958, *Proc. Phys. Soc.* **71**, 566.

Starkweather, H. W., 1960, *J. Polymer Sci.* **45**, 525.

Stevels, J. M., 1962, *in* Handbuch der Physik (Berlin: Springer), Vol. 13, p. 510.

Stockmayer, W. H., and Hecht, C. E., 1953, *J. Chem. Phys.* **21**, 1954.

Stoner, E. C., 1936*a*, *Phil. Mag.* **21**, 145.

Stoner, E. C., 1936*b*, *Proc. Roy. Soc.* **A154**, 656.

Stoner, E. C., 1939, *Phil. Mag.* **28**, 257.

Stratton, R., 1953, *Phil. Mag.* **44**, 519.

Stratton, R., 1962, *J. Chem. Phys.* **37**, 2972.

Szigeti, B., 1950, *Proc. Roy. Soc.* **A204**, 51.

Taylor, A. R., Gardner, T. E., and Smith, D. F., 1963, Bureau of Mines Rep. No. 6157 (U. S. Department of the Interior).

Thirring, H., 1913, *Phys. Z.* **14**, 867.

Thompson, A. M., 1958, *IRE Trans. Instr.* **1-7**, 245.

Thurston, R. N., 1967, *J. Acoust. Soc. Am.* **41**, 1093.

Tosi, M. P., and Fumi, G. G., 1963, *Phys. Rev.* **131**, 1458.

Turner, P. S., 1946, *J. Res. Nat. Bur. Std.* **37**, 239.

Vallin, J., Beckman, O., and Salama, K., 1964, *J. Appl. Phys.* **35**, 1222.

Vallin, J., Marklund, K., and Sikström, J. O., 1966, *Ark. Fys. (Sweden)* **33**, 345.

Voronov, F. F., and Goncharova, V. A., 1966, *Soviet Phys.—JETP* **23**, 777.

Voronov, F. F., Goncharova, V. A., and Agapova, T. A., 1967, *Soviet Phys.--Solid State* **8**, 2726.

Wallace, D. C., 1965, *Phys. Rev.* **139**, A877.

Warfield, R. W., and Petree, M. C., 1962, *Nature* **193**, 1280.

Waterhouse, N., and Yates, B., 1968, *Cryogenics* **8**, 267.

Westrum, E. F., Unpublished results.

Westrum, E. F., 1956, IVme Congrès International du Verre, Paris.

White, G. K., 1961*a*, *Cryogenics* **1**, 151.

White, G. K., 1961*b*, *Phil. Mag.* **6**, 815.

White, G. K., 1961*c*, *Phil. Mag.* **6**, 1425.

White, G. K., 1962*a*, *Phil. Mag.* **7**, 271.

White, G. K., 1962*b*, *Cryogenics* **2**, 292.

White, G. K., 1964*a*, *Cryogenics* **4**, 2.

White, G. K., 1964*b*, *Phys. Lett.* **8**, 294.

White, G. K., 1965, *Proc. Phys. Soc.* **86**, 159.

White, G. K., 1969, *J. Phys. C (Solid State Phys.)* **2**, 575.

White, G. K., and Birch, J. A., 1965, *Phys. Chem. Glasses* **6**, 85.

Wohlfarth, E. P., 1948, *Proc. Phys. Soc.* **60**, 360.

Wohlfarth, E. P., 1949, *Proc. Roy. Soc.* **A195**, 434.

Wohlfarth, E. P., 1969, *Phys. Lett.* **28A**, 569.

Wong, C., and Schuele, D. E., 1967, *J. Phys. Chem. Solids* **28**, 1225.

Yates, B., 1966, *Phil. Mag.* **14**, 179.

Yates, B., and Panter, C. H., 1962, *Proc. Phys. Soc.* **80**, 373.

Ziman, J. M., 1964, Electrons in Metals. A Short Guide to the Fermi Surface (London: Taylor and Francis).

Index